D0108754

100 Poems about people

SELECTED BY

ELINOR PARKER

Illustrated by Ismar David

THOMAS Y. CROWELL COMPANY
NEW YORK

*For permission to reprint the copyrighted poems i
this anthology, acknowledgment is extended to th
following:*

Devin Adair Company: for "An Old Woman of the Roads," from C¢
lected Poems, by Padraic Colum.

The Bobbs-Merrill Company, Inc.: for "Old John Henry," from Poer
Here at Home, by James Whitcomb Riley.

Constable and Company Ltd.: for "Love in the Valley" and "Juggli
Jerry," by George Meredith.

The Cresset Press Ltd.: for "To a Fat Lady Seen from the Train," fro
Collected Poems, by Frances Cornford.

Doubleday & Company, Inc.: with Harold Ober Associates, for "The
Lived a Lady in Milan," from Man Possessed, by William Rose Ben¢
copyright 1927 by Doubleday & Company, Inc.; with Methuen & Co
pany, Ltd. and Sir Alan Herbert, for "The Queen in Parliament," fro
Leave My Old Morale Alone, by A. P. Herbert, copyright 1940, 1948
Alan Patrick Herbert; with Ernest Benn Ltd. and Sir Alan Herbert, f
"Laughing Ann," from Laughing Ann and Other Poems (A Book
Ballads), by A. P. Herbert, copyright 1920 by Doubleday & Compar
Inc.; for "Martin," from Trees and Other Poems, by Joyce Kilmer, coj
right 1914 by Doubleday & Company, Inc.; with The Macmillan Co
pany of Canada, Ltd. and Mrs. George Bambridge, for "The Looki
Glass," from Rewards and Fairies, by Rudyard Kipling, copyright
Rudyard Kipling; and for "My Rival," from Departmental Ditties a
Ballads and Barrack-Room Ballads, by Rudyard Kipling; with Ann Wol
for "The Old Lady," from Kensington Gardens, by Humbert Wolfe.

E. P. Dutton & Company, Inc.: with Jonathan Cape, Ltd. and the Ma
Webb Estate, for "Anne's Book," from Poems, by Mary Webb.

Eleanor Farjeon: for "Henry VIII," from Kings and Queens, by Elear
and Herbert Farjeon; for "Rob Roy" and "Sir Philip Sidney," fro
Heroes and Heroines, by Eleanor and Herbert Farjeon.

Henry Holt and Company, Inc.: for "Old Susan" and "An Epitaph," from *Collected Poems*, by Walter de la Mare, copyright 1920 by Henry Holt and Company, Inc., copyright 1948 by Walter de la Mare; for "Tired Tim," from *Poems for Children*, by Walter de la Mare, copyright 1930 by Henry Holt and Company, Inc.; for "An Old Man's Winter Night," from *Mountain Interval*, by Robert Frost, copyright 1916, 1921 by Henry Holt and Company, Inc., copyright 1944 by Robert Frost; for "Gone," from *Chicago Poems*, by Carl Sandburg, copyright 1916 by Henry Holt and Company, Inc., copyright 1944 by Carl Sandburg.

Houghton Mifflin Company: for "Songs for My Mother," by Anna Hempstead Branch.

Alfred A. Knopf, Inc.: with A. D. Peters, for "Charles Augustus Fortescue," from *Cautionary Verses*, by Hilaire Belloc.

J. B. Lippincott Company: for "Fred," from *Poems for Children*, by Eleanor Farjeon, copyright 1951 by Eleanor Farjeon.

Longmans, Green & Company, Inc.: for "The Clerk of Oxenford," from *Chaucer's Canterbury Tales*, edited by Frank Ernest Hill.

The Macmillan Company: for "John Popham," from *Saltwater Farm*, by Robert P. T. Coffin; for "Aladdin and the Jinn" and "Abraham Lincoln Walks at Midnight," from *Collected Poems*, by Vachel Lindsay; for "Captain Stratton's Fancy," from *Collected Poems*, by John Masefield; with the Edgar Lee Masters Estate, for "Lucinda Matlock," from *Spoon River Anthology*, by Edgar Lee Masters; with Gerald Duckworth & Company, Ltd., for "Farmer's Bride," from *Collected Poems*, by Charlotte Mew; with The Macmillan Company of Canada Ltd. and Mrs. Stephens, for "Deirdre," from *Collected Poems*, by James Stephens.

Mr. Virgil Markham: for "Lincoln, the Man of the People," from *Poems of Edwin Markham*, by Edwin Markham.

The Proprietors of *Punch*: for "Leonardo" and "Voltaire," by E. C. Bentley.

The Richards Press, Ltd.: for "Don Juan Declaims," from *Collected Poems*, by James Elroy Flecker.

Rinehart & Company, Inc.: for "Mountain Woman," from *Skylines and Horizons*, by DuBose Heyward, copyright 1924 by Rinehart & Company, Inc., copyright renewed 1952 by Dorothy Heyward.

Charles Scribner's Sons: for "Miniver Cheevy," from *The Town Down The River*, by Edwin Arlington Robinson, copyright 1910 by Charles Scribner's Sons, 1938 by Ruth Nivison.

Werner Laurie, Ltd.: with Mr. E. C. Bentley, for "Shakespeare" and "Columbus," from *More Biography*, by E. C. Bentley.

Yale University Press: for "A Hill Woman," from *Forgotten Shrines*, by John Farrar.

for E. F. P. with my love

Contents

Under Twenty

My Fair Lady

Lives in Sunshine

Lives in Shadow

From the Hills, from the Roads, from the Sea

"All That's Past"

People from History

From Storybook and Legend

Some Strange Characters

The Poet Himself

Under Twenty

Tired Tim

Poor tired Tim! It's sad for him.
He lags the long bright morning through,
Ever so tired of nothing to do;
He moons and mopes the livelong day,
Nothing to think about, nothing to say;
Up to bed with his candle to creep,
Too tired to yawn, too tired to sleep:
Poor tired Tim! It's sad for him.

WALTER DE LA MARE

Little Blue-Ribbons

'Little Blue-Ribbons!' We call her that
From the ribbons she wears in her favorite hat;
For may not a person be only five,
And yet have the neatest of taste alive?—
As a matter of fact, this one has views
Of the strictest sort as to frocks and shoes;
And we never object to a sash or bow,
When 'little Blue-Ribbons' prefers it so.

'Little Blue-Ribbons' has eyes of blue,
And an arch little mouth, when the teeth peep through;
And her primitive look is wise and grave,
With a sense of the weight of the word 'behave';
Though now and again she may condescend
To a radiant smile for a private friend;
But to smile for ever is weak, you know,
And 'little Blue-Ribbons' regards it so.

She's a staid little woman! and so as well
Is her ladyship's doll, 'Miss Bonnibelle';
But I think what at present the most takes up
The thoughts of her heart is her last new cup;
For the object thereon,—be it understood,—
Is the 'Robin that buried the "Babes in the Wood" '—
It is not in the least like a robin, though,
But 'little Blue-Ribbons' declares it so.

'Little Blue-Ribbons' believes, I think,
That the rain comes down for the birds to drink;
Moreover, she holds, in a cab you'd get
To the spot where the suns of yesterday set;
And I know that she fully expects to meet
With a lion or wolf in Regent Street!
We may smile, and deny as we like— But, no,
For 'little Blue-Ribbons' still dreams it so.

Dear 'little Blue-Ribbons'! She tells us all
That she never intends to be 'great' and 'tall';
(For how could she ever contrive to sit
In her 'own, own chair,' if she grew one bit!)
And, further, she says, she intends to stay
In her 'darling home' till she gets 'quite gray';
Alas! we are gray; and we doubt, you know,
But 'little Blue-Ribbons' will have it so!

AUSTIN DOBSON

Fred

Fred likes creatures,
And has a lot of 'em.
Bees don't sting him,
He's got a pot of 'em,
Little round velvety bodies they are
Making honey in Fred's jam-jar.

Fred likes creatures.
Hedgehogs don't prickle him,
They flatten their quills
And scarcely tickle him,
But lie with their pointed snouts on his palm,
And their beady eyes are perfectly calm.

Fred likes creatures.
The nestling fallen out
Of the tree-top
With magpie callin' out
Where? Where? Where? contented lingers
In the round nest of Fred's thick fingers.

Fred likes creatures.
Nothing's queer to him,
Ferrets, tortoises,
Newts are dear to him.
The lost wild rabbit comes to his hand
As to a burrow in friendly land.

Fred *eats* rabbit
Like any glutton, too,
Fred eats chicken
And beef and mutton too.
Moral? None. No more to be said
Than Fred likes creatures, and creatures like Fred.

ELEANOR FARJEON

The Barefoot Boy

Blessings on thee, little man,
Barefoot boy, with cheek of tan!
With thy turned-up pantaloons,
And thy merry whistled tunes;
With thy red lip, redder still
Kissed by strawberries on the hill;
With the sunshine on thy face,
Through thy torn brim's jaunty grace;
From my heart I give thee joy,—
I was once a barefoot boy!

Prince thou art,—the grown-up man
Only is republican.
Let the million-dollared ride!
Barefoot, trudging at his side,
Thou hast more than he can buy
In the reach of ear and eye,—
Outward sunshine, inward joy:
Blessings on thee, barefoot boy!

Oh for boyhood's painless play,
Sleep that wakes in laughing day,
Health that mocks the doctor's rules,
Knowledge never learned of schools,
Of the wild bee's morning chase,
Of the wild-flower's time and place,
Flight of fowl and habitude
Of the tenants of the wood;

How the tortoise bears his shell,
How the woodchuck digs his cell,
And the ground-mole sinks his well;
How the robin feeds her young,
How the oriole's nest is hung;
Where the whitest lilies blow,
Where the freshest berries grow,
Where the ground-nut trails its vine,
Where the wood-grape's clusters shine;
Of the black wasp's cunning way,
Mason of his walls of clay,
And the architectural plans
Of gray hornet artisans!
For, eschewing books and tasks,
Nature answers all he asks;
Hand in hand with her he walks,
Face to face with her he talks,
Part and parcel of her joy,—
Blessings on the barefoot boy!

Oh for boyhood's time of June,
Crowding years in one brief moon,
When all things I heard or saw,
Me, their master, waited for.
I was rich in flowers and trees,
Humming-birds and honey-bees;
For my sport the squirrel played,
Plied the snouted mole his spade;
For my taste the blackberry cone
Purpled over hedge and stone;
Laughed the brook for my delight

Through the day and through the night,
Whispering at the garden wall,
Talked with me from fall to fall;
Mine the sand-rimmed pickerel pond,
Mine the walnut slopes beyond,
Mine, on bending orchard trees,
Apples of Hesperides!
Still as my horizon grew,
Larger grew my riches too;
All the world I saw or knew
Seemed a complex Chinese toy,
Fashioned for a barefoot boy!

Oh for festal dainties spread,
Like my bowl of milk and bread;
Pewter spoon and bowl of wood,
On the door-stone, gray and rude!
O'er me, like a regal tent,
Cloudy-ribbed, the sunset bent,
Purple-curtained, fringed with gold,
Looped in many a wind-swung fold;
While for music came the play
Of the pied frogs' orchestra;
And, to light the noisy choir,
Lit the fly his lamp of fire.
I was monarch: pomp and joy
Waited on the barefoot boy!

Cheerily, then, my little man,
Live and laugh, as boyhood can!

Though the flinty slopes be hard,
Stubble-speared the new-mown sward,
Every morn shall lead thee through
Fresh baptisms of the dew;
Every evening from thy feet
Shall the cool wind kiss the heat:
All too soon these feet must hide
In the prison cells of pride,
Lose the freedom of the sod,
Like a colt's for work be shod,
Made to tread the mills of toil,
Up and down in ceaseless moil:
Happy if their track be found
Never on forbidden ground;
Happy if they sink not in
Quick and treacherous sands of sin.
Ah! that thou couldst know thy joy,
Ere it passes, barefoot boy!

JOHN GREENLEAF WHITTIER

Charles Augustus Fortescue

Who always Did what was Right,
and so accumulated an Immense Fortune

The nicest child I ever knew
Was Charles Augustus Fortescue.
He never lost his cap, or tore
His stockings or his pinafore:
In eating Bread he made no Crumbs,
He was extremely fond of sums,
To which, however, he preferred
The Parsing of a Latin Word—
He sought, when it was in his power,
For information twice an hour,
And as for finding Mutton-Fat
Unappetising, far from that!
He often, at his Father's Board,
Would beg them, of his own accord,
To give him, if they did not mind,
The Greasiest Morsels they could find—
His Later Years did not belie
The Promise of his Infancy.
In Public Life he always tried
To take a judgment Broad and Wide;
In Private, none was more than he
Renowned for quiet courtesy.
He rose at once in his Career,
And long before his Fortieth Year
Had wedded Fifi, Only Child
Of Bunyan, First Lord Aberfylde.

He thus became immensely Rich,
And built the Splendid Mansion which
Is called "The Cedars, Muswell Hill,"
Where he resides in Affluence still,
To show what Everybody might
Become by
    Simply Doing Right.

HILAIRE BELLOC

Dorothy Q.

Grandmother's mother: her age, I guess,
Thirteen summers, or something less;
Girlish bust, but womanly air,
Smooth, square forehead with uprolled hair,
Lips that lover has never kissed;
Taper fingers and slender wrist;
Hanging sleeves of stiff brocade;
So they painted the little maid.

On her hand a parrot green
Sits unmoving and broods serene.
Hold up the canvas full in view,—
Look! there's a rent the light shines through,
Dark with a century's fringe of dust,—
That was a Red-Coat's rapier thrust!
Such is the tale the lady old,
Dorothy's daughter's daughter, told.

Who the painter was none may tell,—
One whose best was not over well;
Hard and dry, it must be confessed,
Flat as a rose that has long been pressed;
Yet in her cheek the hues are bright,
Dainty colors of red and white,
And in her slender shape are seen
Hint and promise of stately mien.

Look not on her with eyes of scorn,—
Dorothy Q. was a lady born!
Ay! Since the galloping Normans came,
England's annals have known her name;
And still to the three-hilled rebel town
Dear is that ancient name's renown,
For many a civic wreath they won,
The youthful sire and the gray-haired son.

O Damsel Dorothy! Dorothy Q.!
Strange is the gift I owe to you;
Such a gift as never a king
Save to daughter or son might bring,—
All my tenure of heart and hand,
All my title to house and land;
Mother and sister and child and wife
And joy and sorrow and death and life!

What if a hundred years ago
Those close-shut lips had answered No,
When forth the tremulous questions came
That cost the maiden her Norman name,
And under the folds that look so still
The bodice swelled with the bosom's thrill?
Should I be I, or would it be
One tenth another, to nine-tenths me?

Soft is the breath of a maiden's YES:
Not the light gossamer stirs with less;
But never a cable that holds so fast
Through all the battles of wave and blast,

And never an echo of speech or song
That lives in the babbling air so long!
There were tones in the voice that whispered then
You may hear today in a hundred men.

O lady and lover, how faint and far
Your images hover,—and here we are,
Solid and stirring in flesh and bone,—
Edward's and Dorothy's—all their own,—
A goodly record for Time to show
Of a syllable spoken so long ago!—
Shall I bless you, Dorothy, or forgive
For the tender whisper that bade me live?

It shall be a blessing, my little maid!
I will heal the stab of the Red-Coat's blade,
And freshen the gold of the tarnished frame,
And gild with a rhyme your household name;
So you shall smile on us brave and bright
As first you greeted the morning's light,
And live untroubled by woes and fears
Through a second youth of a hundred years.

OLIVER WENDELL HOLMES

Anne's Book

And so, Anne Everard, in those leafy Junes
Long withered; in those ancient, dark Decembers,
Deep in the drift of time, haunted by tunes
Long silent; you, beside the homely embers,
Or in some garden fragrant and precise
Were diligent and attentive all day long!
Fashioning with bright wool and stitches nice
Your sampler, did you hear the thrushes' song
Wistfully? While, in orderly array,
Six rounded trees grew up; the alphabet,
Stout and uncompromising, done in grey;
The Lord's Prayer, and your age, in violet;
Did you, Anne Everard, dream from hour to hour
How the young wind was crying on the hill,
And the young world was breaking into flower?
With small head meekly bent, all mute and still,
Earnest to win the promised great reward,
Did you not see the birds, at shadow-time,
Come hopping all across the dewy sward?
Did you not hear the bells of Faery chime
Liquidly, where the brittle hyacinths grew?
Your dream—attention; diligence, your aim!
And when the last long needleful was through,
When, labored for so long, the guerdon came—
Thomson, his *Seasons*, neatly bound in green—
How brightly would the golden letters shine!
Ah! many a petalled May the moon has seen
Since Anne—attentive, diligent, *aetat* nine—

Puckering her young brow, read the stately phrases.
Sampler and book are here without a stain—
Only Anne Everard lies beneath the daisies;
Only Anne Everard will not come again.

MARY WEBB

My Rival

I go to concert, party, ball—
    What profit is in these?
I sit alone against the wall
    And strive to look at ease.
The incense that is mine by right
    They burn before Her shrine;
And that's because I'm seventeen
    And she is forty-nine.

I cannot check my girlish blush,
    My colour comes and goes.
I redden to my finger-tips,
    And sometimes to my nose.
But She is white where white should be,
    And red where red should shine.
The blush that flies at seventeen
    Is fixed at forty-nine.

I wish *I* had her constant cheek:
    I wish that I could sing
All sorts of funny little songs,
    Not quite the proper thing.
I'm very *gauche* and very shy,
    Her jokes aren't in my line;
And, worst of all, I'm seventeen
    While She is forty-nine.

The young men come, the young men go,
  Each pink and white and neat,
She's older than their mothers, but
  They grovel at Her feet.
They walk beside Her *'rickshaw*-wheels—
  None ever walk by mine;
And that's because I'm seventeen
  And She is forty-nine.

She rides with half a dozen men
  (She calls them "boys" and "mashes"),
I trot along the Mall alone;
  My prettiest frocks and sashes
Don't help to fill my programme-card,
  And vainly I repine
From ten to two A.M. Ah me!
  Would I were forty-nine.

She calls me "darling," "pet," and "dear,"
  And "sweet retiring maid."
I'm always at the back, I know—
  She puts me in the shade.
She introduces me to men—
  "Cast" lovers, I opine;
For sixty takes to seventeen,
  Nineteen to forty-nine.

But even She must older grow
  And end Her dancing days,
She can't go on for ever so
  At concerts, balls, and plays.

One ray of priceless hope I see
    Before my footsteps shine;
Just think, that She'll be eighty-one
    When I am forty-nine!

RUDYARD KIPLING

Jane and Eliza

There were two little girls, neither handsome nor plain,
One's name was Eliza, the other was Jane;
They were both of one height, as I've heard people say,
And both of one age, I believe, to a day.

'Twas fancied by some, who but slightly had seen them,
There was not a pin to be chosen between them;
But no one for long in this notion persisted,
So great a distinction there *really* existed.

Eliza knew well that she could not be pleasing,
While fretting and fuming, while sulking or teasing;
And therefore in company artfully tried,
Not to break her bad habits, but only to *hide.*

So, when she was out, with much labor and pain,
She contrived to look *almost* as pleasant as Jane;
But then you might see that, in forcing a smile,
Her mouth was uneasy and ached all the while.

And in spite of her care it would sometimes befall
That some cross event happened to ruin it all;
And because it might chance that her share was the
    worst,
Her temper broke loose, and her dimples dispersed.

But Jane, who had nothing she wanted to hide,
And therefore these troublesome arts never tried,
Had none of the care and fatigue of concealing,
But her face always showed what her bosom was feeling.

At home or abroad there was peace in her smile,
A cheerful good nature that needed no guile.
And Eliza worked hard, but could never obtain
The affection that freely was given to Jane.

ANN TAYLOR

There Was a Little Girl

There was a little girl, who had a little curl
   Right in the middle of her forehead,
And when she was good, she was very, very good,
   But when she was bad she was horrid.

She stood on her head, on her little trundle-bed,
   With nobody by for to hinder;
She screamed and she squalled, she yelled and she
    bawled,
   And drummed her little heels against the winder.

Her mother heard the noise, and thought it was the
    boys
   Playing in the empty attic,
She rushed upstairs, and caught her unawares,
   And spanked her, most emphatic.

HENRY WADSWORTH LONGFELLOW

My Fair Lady

Silvia

Who is Silvia? What is she?
   That all our swains commend her?
Holy, fair, and wise is she;
   The heaven such grace did lend her,
That she might admired be.

Is she kind as she is fair?
   For beauty lives with kindness:
Love doth to her eyes repair,
   To help him of his blindness;
And, being helped, inhabits there.

Then to Silvia let us sing,
   That Silvia is excelling;
She excels each mortal thing
   Upon the dull earth dwelling:
To her let us garlands bring.

WILLIAM SHAKESPEARE

"Three Years She Grew"

Three years she grew in sun and shower,
Then Nature said, "A lovelier flower
On earth was never sown;
This Child I to myself will take;
She shall be mine, and I will make
A Lady of my own.

"Myself will to my darling be
Both law and impulse; and with me
The Girl, in rock and plain,
In earth and heaven, in glade and bower,
Shall feel an overseeing power
To kindle or restrain.

"She shall be sportive as the fawn
That wild with glee across the lawn,
Or up the mountain springs;
And hers shall be the breathing balm,
And hers the silence and the calm
Of mute insensate things.

"The floating clouds their state shall lend
To her; for her the willow bend;
Nor shall she fail to see
Even in the motions of the Storm
Grace that shall mould the Maiden's form
By silent sympathy.

"The stars of midnight shall be dear
To her; and she shall lean her ear
In many a secret place
Where rivulets dance their wayward round,
And beauty born of murmuring sound
Shall pass into her face.

"And vital feelings of delight
Shall rear her form to stately height,
Her virgin bosom swell;
Such thoughts to Lucy I will give
While she and I together live
Here in this happy dell."

Thus Nature spake—the work was done—
How soon my Lucy's race was run!
She died, and left to me
This heath, this calm and quiet scene;
The memory of what has been,
And never more will be.

WILLIAM WORDSWORTH

"She Was a Phantom of Delight"

She was a Phantom of delight
When first she gleamed upon my sight;
A lovely Apparition, sent
To be a moment's ornament;
Her eyes as stars of Twilight fair;
Like Twilight's, too, her dusky hair;
But all things else about her drawn
From May-time and the cheerful dawn;
A dancing Shape, an Image gay,
To haunt, to startle, and way-lay.

I saw her upon nearer view,
A Spirit, yet a Woman too!
Her household motions light and free,
And steps of virgin-liberty;
A countenance in which did meet
Sweet records, promises as sweet;
A Creature not too bright or good
For human nature's daily food;
For transient sorrows, simple wiles,
Praise, blame, love, kisses, tears, and smiles.

And now I see with eye serene
The very pulse of the machine;
A Being breathing thoughtful breath,
A Traveller between life and death;
The reason firm, the temperate will,
Endurance, foresight, strength, and skill;

A perfect Woman, nobly planned,
To warn, to comfort, and command;
And yet a Spirit still, and bright
With something of angelic light.

WILLIAM WORDSWORTH

She Walks in Beauty

She walks in beauty, like the night
   Of cloudless climes and starry skies;
And all that's best of dark and bright
   Meet in her aspect and her eyes:
Thus mellowed to that tender light
   Which heaven to gaudy day denies.

One shade the more, one ray the less,
   Had half impaired the nameless grace
Which waves in every raven tress,
   Or softly lightens o'er her face;
Where thoughts serenely sweet express
   How pure, how dear their dwelling-place.

And on that cheek, and o'er that brow,
   So soft, so calm, yet eloquent,
The smiles that win, the tints that glow,
   But tell of days in goodness spent,
A mind at peace with all below,
   A heart whose love is innocent.

LORD BYRON

FROM Love in the Valley

Under yonder beech-tree single on the green-sward,
  Couch'd with her arms behind her golden head,
Knees and tresses folded to slip and ripple idly,
  Lies my young love sleeping in the shade.
Had I the heart to slide an arm beneath her,
  Press her parting lips as her waist I gather slow,
Waking in amazement she could not but embrace me:
  Then would she hold me and never let me go?

Shy as the squirrel and wayward as the swallow,
  Swift as the swallow along the river's light
Circleting the surface to meet the mirror'd winglets,
  Fleeter she seems in her stay than in her flight.
Shy as the squirrel that leaps among the pine-tops,
  Wayward as the swallow overhead at set of sun,
She whom I love is hard to catch and conquer,
  Hard, but O the glory of the winning were she won!

When her mother tends her before the laughing mirror,
  Tying up her laces, looping up her hair,
Often she thinks, were this wild thing wedded,
  More love should I have, and much less care.
When her mother tends her before the lighted mirror,
  Loosening her laces, combing down her curls,
Often she thinks, were this wild thing wedded,
  I should miss but one for many boys and girls.

Heartless she is as the shadow in the meadows
  Flying to the hills on a blue and breezy noon.
No, she is athirst and drinking up her wonder:
  Earth to her is young as the slip of the new moon.
Deals she an unkindness, 'tis but her rapid measure,
  Even as in a dance; and her smile can heal no less:
Like the swinging May-cloud that pelts the flowers
    with hailstones
  Off a sunny border, she was made to bruise and bless.

Lovely are the curves of the white owl sweeping
  Wavy in the dusk lit by one large star.
Lone on the fir-branch, his rattle-note unvaried,
  Brooding o'er the gloom, spins the brown evejar.
Darker grows the valley, more and more forgetting:
  So were it with me if forgetting could be will'd.
Tell the grassy hollow that holds the bubbling well-
    spring,
  Tell it to forget the source that keeps it fill'd.

Stepping down the hill with her fair companions,
  Arm in arm, all against the raying West,
Boldly she sings, to the merry tune she marches,
  Brave is her shape, and sweeter unpossess'd.
Sweeter, for she is what my heart first awaking
  Whisper'd the world was; morning light is she.
Love that so desires would fain keep her changeless;
  Fain would fling the net, and fain have her free.

Happy happy time, when the white star hovers
　　Low over dim fields fresh with bloomy dew,
Near the face of dawn, that draws athwart the darkness,
　　Threading it with colour, like yewberries the yew.
Thicker crowd the shades as the grave East deepens
　　Glowing, and with crimson a long cloud swells.
Maiden still the morn is; and strange she is, and secret;
　　Strange her eyes; her cheeks are cold as cold sea-
　　　shells.

　　　　　　.　　　.　　　.

Mother of the dews, dark eye-lash'd twilight,
　　Low-lidded twilight, o'er the valley's brim,
Rounding on thy breast sings the dew-delighted skylark,
　　Clear as though the dewdrops had their voice in him.
Hidden where the rose-flush drinks the rayless planet,
　　Fountain-full he pours the spraying fountain-
　　　showers.
Let me hear her laughter, I would have her ever
　　Cool as dew in twilight, the lark above the flowers.

All the girls are out with their baskets for the primrose;
　　Up lanes, woods through, they troop in joyful bands.
My sweet leads: she knows not why, but now she
　　loiters,
　　Eyes the bent anemones, and hangs her hands.
Such a look will tell that the violets are peeping,
　　Coming the rose: and unaware a cry
Springs in her bosom for odours and for colour,
　　Covert and the nightingale; she knows not why.

　　　　　　.　　　.　　　.

Hither she comes; she comes to me; she lingers,
  Deepens her brown eyebrows, while in new surprise
High rise the lashes in wonder of a stranger;
  Yet am I the light and living of her eyes.
Something friends have told her fills her heart to brim-
      ming,
    Nets her in her blushes, and wounds her, and
      tames.—
Sure of her haven, O like a dove alighting,
  Arms up, she dropp'd: our souls were in our names.

Could I find a place to be alone with heaven,
  I would speak my heart out: heaven is my need.
Every woodland tree is flushing like the dogwood,
  Flashing like the whitebeam, swaying like the reed.
Flushing like the dogwood crimson in October;
  Streaming like the flag-reed South-West blown;
Flashing as in gusts the sudden-lighted whitebeam:
  All seem to know what is for heaven alone.

GEORGE MEREDITH

The Shepherdess

She walks—the lady of my delight—
 A shepherdess of sheep.
Her flocks are thoughts. She keeps them white;
 She guards them on the steep;
She feeds them on the fragrant height,
 And folds them in for sleep.

She roams maternal hills and bright,
 Dark valleys safe and deep.
Into that tender breast at night
 The chastest stars may peep.
She walks—the lady of my delight—
 A shepherdess of sheep.

She holds her little thoughts in sight,
 Though gay they run and leap.
She is so circumspect and right;
 She has her soul to keep.
She walks—the lady of my delight—
 A shepherdess of sheep.

ALICE MEYNELL

Laughing Ann

When laughing Ann trips down the street
   The sun comes out as well,
The town is at her twinkling feet,
   The crier rings his bell,
The young men leap like little fish,
   Policemen stand and purr,
While husbands look behind and wish
   That they had married her.

    Laughing Ann
      Turns her head,
   Looks at a man
      And kills him dead
        With eyes that say,
        "What a nice fine day!
    Good morning—this is Ann,
      Never been kissed,
      Born to be kissed,
   But kiss me if you can!"

And when she steps into a shop
   The happy hosier grins,
The lordly haberdashers hop
   To furnish her with pins,
The grocer asks no other fee
   If she will glance his way,
And trembles while he sells her tea
   To think that she must pay.

For laughing Ann
    With innocent eyes
Looks at a man
    And then he dies,
        With eyes that say,
        "And have you, pray,
Seen anything quite like Ann?
        Never been kissed,
        Born to be kissed,
But kiss me if you can!"

Her eyes are like two pools of wine,
    Her cheeks like roses pressed,
Her lips are full, her nose is fine,
    And you can guess the rest;
She is more pure than precious stones,
    And angel is her rank,
But she has married Mr. Jones,
    The manager of the Bank.

    Ah, laughing Ann
        Turns her head,
Looks at a man
        And kills him dead,
        With eyes that say,
        "Behold, I pray,
This unsurpassable Ann!
        But the man who owns
        This jewel is Jones,
So kiss me if you can!"

So when she dances up the street
    And homeward disappears
The young men move with leaden feet,
    Policemen stand in tears,
While butchers with a vicious knife
    Assault their hateful wares,
To think that Mr. Jones's wife
    Can never now be theirs.

    For laughing Ann
        With two bright eyes
    Can kill a man
        Of any size
           With eyes that say,
           "What a nice fine day!
    But Ann is twice as fair,
        Hard to resist,
        Born to be kissed,
    But kiss me if you dare!"

A. P. HERBERT

An Epitaph

Here lies a most beautiful lady:
Light of step and heart was she;
I think she was the most beautiful lady
That ever was in the West Country.
But beauty vanishes; beauty passes;
However rare—rare it be;
And when I crumble, who will remember
This lady of the West Country?

WALTER DE LA MARE

From Life

Her thoughts are like a flock of butterflies.
　　She has a merry love of little things,
　　And a bright flutter of speech, whereto she brings
A threefold eloquence—voice, hands and eyes.
Yet under all a subtle silence lies
　　As a bird's heart is hidden by its wings;
　　And you shall search through many wanderings
The fairyland of her realities.

She hides herself behind a busy brain—
　　A woman, with a child's laugh in her blood;
　　A maid, wearing the shadow of motherhood—
Wise with the quiet memory of old pain,
As the soft glamor of remembered rain
　　Hallows the gladness of a sunlit wood.

BRIAN HOOKER

A Certain Young Lady

There's a certain young lady,
Who's just in her hey-day,
   And full of all mischief, I ween;
      So teasing! so pleasing!
      Capricious! delicious!
   And you know very well whom I mean.

With an eye dark as night,
Yet than noonday more bright,
   Was ever a black eye so keen?
      It can thrill with a glance,
      With a beam can entrance,
   And you know very well whom I mean.

With a stately step—such as
You'd expect in a duchess—
   And a brow might distinguish a queen,
      With a mighty proud air,
      That says "touch me who dare,"
   And you know very well whom I mean.

With a toss of the head
That strikes one quite dead,
   But a smile to revive one again;
      That toss so appalling!
      That smile so enthralling!
   And you know very well whom I mean.

Confound her! de'il take her!—
A cruel heart-breaker—
    But hold! see that smile so serene.
        God love her! God bless her!
        May nothing distress her!
    And you know very well whom I mean.

Heaven help the adorer
Who happens to bore her,
    The lover who wakens her spleen;
        But too blest for a sinner
        Is he who shall win her,
    And you know very well whom I mean.

WASHINGTON IRVING

Lives in Sunshine

The Jolly Old Pedagogue

'Twas a jolly old pedagogue, long ago,
    Tall, and slender, and sallow, and dry;
His form was bent, and his gait was slow,
And his long, thin hair was as white as snow,
    But a wonderful twinkle shone in his eye:
And he sang every night as he went to bed,
    "Let us be happy down here below;
The living should live, though the dead be dead,"
    Said the jolly old pedagoguc, long ago.

He taught the scholars the Rule of Three,
    Reading, and writing, and history, too;
He took the little ones on his knee,
For a kind old heart in his breast had he,
    And the wants of the littlest child he knew.
"Learn while you're young," he often said,
    "There is much to enjoy down here below;
Life for the living, and the rest for the dead!"
    Said the jolly old pedagogue, long ago.

With the stupidest boys, he was kind and cool,
    Speaking only in gentlest tones;
The rod was scarcely known in his school—
Whipping to him was a barbarous rule,
    And too hard work for his poor old bones;
Besides, it was painful, he sometimes said:
    "We should make life pleasant down here below—
The living need charity more than the dead,"
    Said the jolly old pedagogue, long ago.

He lived in the house by the hawthorn lane,
    With roses and woodbine over the door;
His rooms were quiet, and neat, and plain,
But a spirit of comfort there held reign,
    And made him forget he was old and poor.
"I need so little," he often said;
    "And my friends and relatives here below
Won't litigate over me when I am dead,"
    Said the jolly old pedagogue, long ago.

But the pleasantest times of all he had,
    Were the sociable hours he used to pass,
With his chair tipped back to a neighbor's wall,
Making an unceremonious call,
    Over a pipe and a friendly glass:
This was the finest pleasure, he said,
    Of the many he tasted here below.
"Who had no cronies had better be dead,"
    Said the jolly old pedagogue, long ago.

The jolly old pedagogue's wrinkled face
    Melted all over in sunshiny smiles;
He stirred his glass with an old-school grace,
Chuckled, and sipped, and prattled apace,
    Till the house grew merry from cellar to tiles.
"I'm a pretty old man," he gently said,
    "I've lingered a long time here below;
But my heart is fresh, if my youth is fled!"
    Said the jolly old pedagogue, long ago.

He smoked his pipe in the balmy air
   Every night, when the sun went down;
And the soft wind played in his silvery hair,
Leaving its tenderest kisses there,
   On the jolly old pedagogue's jolly old crown;
And feeling the kisses, he smiled, and said:
   " 'Tis a glorious world down here below;
Why wait for happiness till we are dead?"
   Said this jolly old pedagogue, long ago.

He sat at his door one midsummer night,
   After the sun had sunk in the west,
And the lingering beams of golden light
Made his kindly old face look warm and bright,
   While the odorous night-winds whispered,
     "Rest!"
Gently, gently, he bowed his head;
   There were angels waiting for him, I know;
He was sure of his happiness, living or dead;
   This jolly old pedagogue, long ago!

GEORGE ARNOLD

Songs for My Mother

1 *Her Hands*

My mother's hands are cool and fair,
    They can do anything.
 Delicate mercies hide them there
    Like flowers in the spring.

When I was small and could not sleep,
    She used to come to me,
And with my cheek upon her hand
    How sure my rest would be.

For everything she ever touched
    Of beautiful or fine,
Their memories living in her hands
    Would warm that sleep of mine.

Her hands remember how they played
    One time in meadow streams,—
And all the flickering song and shade
    Of water took my dreams.

Swift through her haunted fingers pass
    Memories of garden things;—
I dipped my face in flowers and grass
    And sounds of hidden wings.

One time she touched the cloud that kissed
    Brown pastures bleak and far;—

I leaned my cheek into a mist
  And thought I was a star.

All this was very long ago
  And I am grown; but yet
The hand that lured my slumber so
  I never can forget.

For still when drowsiness comes on
  It seems so soft and cool,
Shaped happily beneath my cheek,
  Hollow and beautiful.

II *Her Words*

My mother has the prettiest tricks
  Of words and words and words.
Her talk comes out as smooth and sleek
  As breasts of singing birds.

She shapes her speech all silver fine
  Because she loves it so.
And her own eyes begin to shine
  To hear her stories grow.

And if she goes to make a call
  Or out to take a walk
We leave our work when she returns
  And run to hear her talk.

We had not dreamed these things were so
  Of sorrow and of mirth.

Her speech is as a thousand eyes
  Through which we see the earth.

God wove a web of loveliness,
  Of clouds and stars and birds,
But made not anything at all
  So beautiful as words.

They shine around our simple earth
  With golden shadowings,
And every common thing they touch
  Is exquisite with wings.

There's nothing poor and nothing small
  But is made fair with them.
They are the hands of living faith
  That touch the garment's hem.

They are as fair as bloom or air,
  They shine like any star,
And I am rich who learned from her
  How beautiful they are.

ANNA HEMPSTEAD BRANCH

The Village Blacksmith

Under a spreading chestnut-tree
The village smithy stands;
The smith, a mighty man is he,
With large and sinewy hands;
And the muscles of his brawny arms
Are strong as iron bands.

His hair is crisp, and black, and long,
His face is like the tan;
His brow is wet with honest sweat,
He earns whate'er he can,
And looks the whole world in the face,
For he owes not any man.

Week in, week out, from morn till night,
You can hear his bellows blow;
You can hear him swing his heavy sledge,
With measured beat and slow,
Like a sexton ringing the village bell,
When the evening sun is low.

And the children coming home from school
Look in at the open door;
They love to see the flaming forge,
And hear the bellows roar,
And catch the burning sparks that fly
Like chaff from a threshing-floor.

He goes on Sunday to the church,
And sits among his boys;
He hears the parson pray and preach,
He hears his daughter's voice
Singing in the village choir,
And it makes his heart rejoice.

It sounds to him like her mother's voice,
Singing in Paradise!
He needs must think of her once more,
How in the grave she lies;
And with his hard, rough hand he wipes
A tear out of his eyes.

Toiling—rejoicing—sorrowing,
Onward through life he goes;
Each morning sees some task begin,
Each evening sees it close;
Something attempted, something done,
Has earned a night's repose.

Thanks, thanks to thee, my worthy friend,
For the lesson thou hast taught!
Thus at the flaming forge of life
Our fortunes must be wrought;
Thus on its sounding anvil shaped
Each burning deed and thought!

HENRY WADSWORTH LONGFELLOW

Martin

When I am tired of earnest men,
  Intense and keen and sharp and clever,
Pursuing fame with brush or pen
  Or counting metal disks forever,
Then from the halls of shadowland
  Beyond the trackless purple sea,
Old Martin's ghost comes back to stand
  Beside my desk and talk to me.

Still on his delicate pale face
  A quizzical thin smile is showing,
His cheeks are wrinkled like fine lace,
  His kind blue eyes are gay and glowing.
He wears a brilliant-hued cravat,
  A suit to match his soft gray hair,
A rakish stick, a knowing hat,
  A manner blithe and debonair.

How good, that he who always knew
  That being lovely was a duty,
Should have gold halls to wander through,
  And should himself inhabit beauty.
How like his old unselfish way
  To leave those halls of splendid mirth,
And comfort those condemned to stay
  Upon the bleak and somber earth.

Some people ask: What cruel chance
    Made Martin's life so sad a story?
Martin? Why, he exhaled romance
    And wore an overcoat of glory.
A fleck of sunlight in the street,
    A horse, a book, a girl who smiled,—
Such visions made each moment sweet
    For this receptive, ancient child.

Because it was old Martin's lot
    To be, not make, a decoration,
Shall we then scorn him, having not
    His genius of appreciation?
Rich joy and love he got and gave;
    His heart was merry as his dress.
Pile laurel leaves upon his grave
    Who did not gain, but was, success.

JOYCE KILMER

Lucinda Matlock

I went to the dances at Chandlerville,
And played snap-out at Winchester.
One time we changed partners,
Driving home in the moonlight of middle June,
And then I found Davis.
We were married and lived together for seventy years,
Enjoying, working, raising the twelve children,
Eight of whom we lost
Ere I had reached the age of sixty.
I spun, I wove, I kept the house, I nursed the sick,
I made the garden, and for holiday
Rambled over the fields where sang the larks,
And by Spoon River gathering many a shell,
And many a flower and medicinal weed—
Shouting to the wooded hills, singing to the green
    valleys.
At ninety-six I had lived enough, that is all,
And passed to a sweet repose.
What is this I hear of sorrow and weariness,
Anger, discontent and drooping hopes?
Degenerate sons and daughters,
Life is too strong for you—
It takes life to love Life.

EDGAR LEE MASTERS

There Was a Jolly Miller

There was a jolly miller once lived on the river Dee;
He danced and sang from morn till night, no lark as blith
   as he;
And this the burden of his song forever used to be:—
"I care for nobody, no not I, if nobody cares for me.

"I live by my mill, God bless her! she's kindred, child, an
   wife;
I would not change my station for any other in life;
No lawyer, surgeon or doctor e'er had a groat from me;
I care for nobody, no not I, if nobody cares for me."

When spring begins his merry career, oh, how his hea
   grows gay;
No summer's drought alarms his fear, nor winter's co
   decay;
No foresight mars the miller's joy, who's wont to sing an
   say,
"Let others toil from year to year, I live from day to day

Thus, like the miller, bold and free, let us rejoice and sin
The days of youth are made for glee, and time is on the win
This song shall pass from me to thee, along the jovial rin
Let heart and voice and all agree to say, "Long live th
   king."

ISAAC BICKERSTA

Lives

in

Shadow

The Solitary Reaper

Behold her, single in the field,
Yon solitary Highland Lass!
Reaping and singing by herself;
Stop here, or gently pass!
Alone she cuts and binds the grain,
And sings a melancholy strain;
O listen! for the Vale profound
Is overflowing with the sound.

No Nightingale did ever chant
More welcome notes to weary bands
Of travellers in some shady haunt,
Among Arabian sands:
A voice so thrilling ne'er was heard
In spring-time from the Cuckoo-bird,
Breaking the silence of the seas
Among the farthest Hebrides.

Will no one tell me what she sings?—
Perhaps the plaintive numbers flow
For old, unhappy, far-off things,
And battles long ago:
Or is it some more humble lay,
Familiar matter of to-day?
Some natural sorrow, loss, or pain,
That has been, and may be again?

Whate'er the theme, the maiden sang
As if her song could have no ending;
I saw her singing at her work,
And o'er the sickle bending;—
I listened, motionless and still;
And, as I mounted up the hill,
The music in my ear I bore
Long after it was heard no more.

WILLIAM WORDSWORTH

Mariana

'Mariana in the moated grange.'
—MEASURE FOR MEASURE

With blackest moss the flower-plots
    Were thickly crusted, one and all:
The rusted nails fell from the knots
    That held the pear to the gable-wall.
The broken sheds look'd sad and strange:
    Unlifted was the clinking latch;
    Weeded and worn the ancient thatch
Upon the lonely moated grange.
      She only said, 'My life is dreary,
        He cometh not,' she said;
      She said, 'I am aweary, aweary,
        I would that I were dead!'

Her tears fell with the dews at even;
    Her tears fell ere the dews were dried;
She could not look on the sweet heaven,
    Either at morn or eventide.
After the flitting of the bats,
    When thickest dark did trance the sky,
    She drew her casement-curtain by,
And glanced athwart the glooming flats.
      She only said, 'The night is dreary,
        He cometh not,' she said;
      She said, 'I am aweary, aweary,
        I would that I were dead!'

Upon the middle of the night,
  Waking she heard the night-fowl crow;
The cock sung out an hour ere light:
  From the dark fen the oxen's low
Came to her: without hope of change,
  In sleep she seem'd to walk forlorn,
  Till cold winds woke the gray-eyed morn
About the lonely moated grange.
    She only said, 'The day is dreary,
      He cometh not,' she said;
    She said, 'I am aweary, aweary,
      I would that I were dead!'

About a stone-cast from the wall
  A sluice with blacken'd waters slept,
And o'er it many, round and small,
  The cluster'd marish-mosses crept.
Hard by a poplar shook alway,
  All silver-green with gnarlèd bark:
  For leagues no other tree did mark
The level waste, the rounding gray.
    She only said, 'My life is dreary,
      He cometh not,' she said;
    She said, 'I am aweary, aweary,
      I would that I were dead!'

And ever when the moon was low,
  And the shrill winds were up and away,
In the white curtain, to and fro,
  She saw the gusty shadow sway.

But when the moon was very low,
   And wild winds bound within their cell,
   The shadow of the poplar fell
Upon her bed, across her brow.
     She only said, 'The night is dreary,
       He cometh not,' she said;
     She said, 'I am aweary, aweary,
       I would that I were dead!'

All day within the dreamy house,
   The doors upon their hinges creak'd;
The blue fly sung in the pane; the mouse
   Behind the mouldering wainscot shriek'd,
Or from the crevice peer'd about.
   Old faces glimmer'd thro' the doors,
   Old footsteps trod the upper floors,
Old voices called her from without.
     She only said, 'My life is dreary,
       He cometh not,' she said;
     She said, 'I am aweary, aweary,
       I would that I were dead!'

The sparrow's chirrup on the roof,
   The slow clock ticking, and the sound
Which to the wooing wind aloof
   The poplar made, did all confound
Her sense; but most she loathed the hour
   When the thick-moted sunbeam lay
   Athwart the chambers, and the day
Was sloping toward his western bower.

Then, said she, 'I am very dreary,
  He will not come,' she said;
She wept, 'I am aweary, aweary,
  Oh God, that I were dead!'

ALFRED   TENNYSON

My Last Duchess

That's my last Duchess painted on the wall,
Looking as if she were alive. I call
That piece a wonder, now: Frà Pandolf's hands
Worked busily a day, and there she stands.
Will't please you sit and look at her? I said
'Frà Pandolf' by design, for never read
Strangers like you that pictured countenance,
The depth and passion of its earnest glance,
But to myself they turned (since none puts by
The curtain I have drawn for you, but I)
And seemed as they would ask me, if they durst,
How such a glance came there; so, not the first
Are you to turn and ask thus. Sir, 'twas not
Her husband's presence only, called that spot
Of joy into the Duchess' cheek: perhaps
Frà Pandolf chanced to say 'Her mantle laps
'Over my lady's wrist too much,' or 'Paint
'Must never hope to reproduce the faint
'Half-flush that dies along her throat:' such stuff
Was courtesy, she thought, and cause enough
For calling up that spot of joy. She had
A heart—how shall I say?—too soon made glad,
Too easily impressed; she liked whate'er
She looked on, and her looks went everywhere.
Sir, 'twas all one! My favour at her breast,
The dropping of the daylight in the West,
The bough of cherries some officious fool
Broke in the orchard for her, the white mule

She rode with round the terrace—all and each
Would draw from her alike the approving speech,
Or blush, at least. She thanked men,—good! but
  thanked
Somehow—I know not how—as if she ranked
My gift of a nine-hundred-years-old name
With anybody's gift. Who'd stoop to blame
This sort of trifling? Even had you skill
In speech—(which I have not)—to make your will
Quite clear to such an one, and say, 'Just this
'Or that in you disgusts me; here you miss,
'Or there exceed the mark'—and if she let
Herself be lessoned so, nor plainly set
Her wits to yours, forsooth, and made excuse,
—E'en then would be some stooping; and I choose
Never to stoop. Oh sir, she smiled, no doubt,
Whene'er I passed her; but who passed without
Much the same smile? This grew; I gave commands;
Then all smiles stopped together. There she stands
As if alive. Will't please you rise? We'll meet
The company below, then. I repeat,
The Count your master's known munificence
Is ample warrant that no just pretence
Of mine for dowry will be disallowed;
Though his fair daughter's self, as I avowed
At starting, is my object. Nay, we'll go
Together down, sir. Notice Neptune, though,
Taming a sea-horse, thought a rarity,
Which Claus of Innsbruck cast in bronze for me!

ROBERT BROWNING

Miniver Cheevy

Miniver Cheevy, child of scorn,
   Grew lean while he assailed the seasons;
He wept that he was ever born,
   And he had reasons.

Miniver loved the days of old
   When swords were bright and steeds were
      prancing;
The vision of a warrior bold
   Would set him dancing.

Miniver sighed for what was not,
   And dreamed, and rested from his labors;
He dreamed of Thebes and Camelot,
   And Priam's neighbors.

Miniver mourned the ripe renown
   That made many a name so fragrant;
He mourned Romance, now on the town,
   And Art, a vagrant.

Miniver loved the Medici,
   Albeit he had never seen one;
He would have sinned incessantly
   Could he have been one.

Miniver cursed the commonplace
   And eyed a khaki suit with loathing;
He missed the mediaeval grace
   Of iron clothing.

Miniver scorned the gold he sought,
  But sore annoyed was he without it;
Miniver thought, and thought, and thought,
  And thought about it.

Miniver Cheevy, born too late,
  Scratched his head and kept on thinking;
Miniver coughed, and called it fate,
  And kept on drinking.

EDWIN ARLINGTON ROBINSON

Richard Cory

When Richard Cory went down town,
We people on the pavement looked at him:
He was a gentleman from sole to crown,
Clean favored, and imperially slim.

And he was always quietly arrayed,
And he was always human when he talked;
But still he fluttered pulses when he said,
"Good-morning," and he glittered when he walked.

And he was rich—yes, richer than a king—
And admirably schooled in every grace:
In fine, we thought that he was everything
To make us wish that we were in his place.

So on we worked, and waited for the light,
And went without the meat, and cursed the bread;
And Richard Cory, one calm summer night,
Went home and put a bullet through his head.

EDWIN ARLINGTON ROBINSON

Gone

Everybody loved Chick Lorimer in our town
                    Far off.
            Everybody loved her.
So we all love a wild girl keeping a hold
            On a dream she wants.
Nobody knows now where Chick Lorimer went.
Nobody knows why she packed her trunk . . . a
    few old things
And is gone,
                    Gone with her little chin
                    Thrust ahead of her
                    And her soft hair blowing careless
                    From under a wide hat,
Dancer, singer, a laughing passionate lover.

Were there ten men or a hundred hunting Chick?
Were there five men or fifty with aching hearts?
            Everybody loved Chick Lorimer.
                Nobody knows where she's gone.

CARL SANDBURG

The Farmer's Bride

Three summers since I chose a maid,—
Too young maybe—but more's to do
At harvest time than bide and woo.
   When us was wed she turned afraid
Of love and me and all things human;
Like the shut of a winter's day.
Her smile went out, and 'twasn't a woman—
   More like a little frightened fay.
   One night, in the fall, she runned away.

"Out 'mong the sheep, her be," they said.
Should properly have been abed;
But sure enough she wasn't there
Lying awake with her wide brown stare.
So over seven-acre field and up-along the down
We chased her, flying like a hare
Before our lanterns. To Church-town
All in a shiver and a scare
We caught her, fetched her home at last
And turned the key upon her, fast.

She does the work about the house
As well as most, but like a mouse:
   Happy enough to chat and play
   With birds and rabbits and such as they,
   So long as men-folk keep away.

"Not near, not near!" her eyes beseech
When one of us comes within reach.
    The women say that beasts in stall
    Look round like children at her call.
    I've hardly heard her speak at all.

Shy as a leveret, swift as he;
Straight and slight as a young larch tree;
Sweet as the first wild violets, she,
To her wild self. But what to me?
The short days shorten and the oaks are brown,
    The blue smoke rises to the low grey sky,
One leaf in the still air falls slowly down,
    A magpie's spotted feathers lie
On the black earth spread white with rime,
The berries ripen up to Christmas-time.
    What's Christmas-time without there be
    Some other in the house than we!

    She sleeps up in the attic there
    Alone, poor maid. 'Tis but a stair
    Betwixt us. Oh, my God!—the down,
    The soft young down of her; the brown,
The brown of her—her eyes, her hair, her hair!

CHARLOTTE MEW

74

We Are Seven

A simple Child,
That lightly draws its breath,
And feels its life in every limb,
What should it know of death?

I met a little cottage Girl:
She was eight years old, she said;
Her hair was thick with many a curl
That clustered round her head.

She had a rustic, woodland air,
And she was wildly clad;
Her eyes were fair, and very fair;
—Her beauty made me glad.

"Sisters and brothers, little maid,
How many may you be?"
"How many? Seven in all," she said,
And wondering looked at me.

"And where are they? I pray you tell."
She answered, "Seven are we;
And two of us at Conway dwell.
And two are gone at sea.

"Two of us in the church-yard lie,
My sister and my brother;
And, in the church-yard cottage, I
Dwell near them with my mother."

"You say that two at Conway dwell,
And two are gone to sea,
Yet ye are seven! I pray you tell,
Sweet Maid, how this may be."

Then did the little Maid reply,
"Seven boys and girls are we;
Two of us in the church-yard lie,
Beneath the church-yard tree."

"You run about, my little Maid,
Your limbs they are alive;
If two are in the church-yard laid,
Then ye are only five."

"Their graves are green, they may be seen,"
The little Maid replied,
"Twelve steps or more from my mother's door,
And they are side by side.

"My stockings there I often knit,
My kerchief there I hem;
And there upon the ground I sit,
And sing a song to them.

"And often after sunset, Sir,
When it is light and fair,
I take my little porringer,
And eat my supper there.

"The first that died was sister Jane;
In bed she moaning lay,

Till God released her of her pain;
And then she went away.

"So in the church-yard she was laid;
And, when the grass was dry,
Together round her grave we played,
My brother John and I.

"And when the ground was white with snow,
And I could run and slide,
My brother John was forced to go,
And he lies by her side."

"How many are you then," said I,
"If they two are in heaven!"
Quick was the little Maid's reply,
"O Master! we are seven."

"But they are dead; those two are dead!
Their spirits are in heaven!"
'Twas throwing words away; for still
The little Maid would have her will,
And said, "Nay, we are seven!"

WILLIAM WORDSWORTH

To a Fat Lady Seen from the Train

O why do you walk through the fields in gloves,
  Missing so much and so much?
O fat white woman whom nobody loves,
Why do you walk through the fields in gloves,
When the grass is soft as the breast of doves
  And shivering sweet to the touch?
O why do you walk through the fields in gloves,
  Missing so much and so much?

FRANCES CORNFORD

"Is My Team Ploughing?"

'Is my team ploughing,
   That I used to drive
And hear the harness jingle
   When I was man alive?'

Ay, the horses trample,
   The harness jingles now;
No change though you lie under
   The land you used to plough,

'Is football playing
   Along the river shore,
With lads to chase the leather,
   Now I stand up no more?'

Ay, the ball is flying,
   The lads play heart and soul,
The goal stands up, the keeper
   Stands up to keep the goal.

'Is my girl happy,
   That I thought hard to leave,
And has she tired of weeping
   As she lies down at eve?'

Ay, she lies down lightly,
   She lies not down to weep:
Your girl is well contented.
   Be still, my lad, and sleep.

'Is my friend hearty,
    Now I am thin and pine,
And has he found to sleep in
    A better bed than mine?'

Yes, lad, I lie easy,
    I lie as lads would choose;
I cheer a dead man's sweetheart,
    Never ask me whose.

A. E. HOUSMAN

The Solitary-Hearted

She was a queen of noble Nature's crowning,
A smile of hers was like an act of grace;
She had no winsome looks, no pretty frowning,
Like daily beauties of the vulgar race:
But if she smiled, a light was on her face,
A clear, cool kindliness, a lunar beam
Of peaceful radiance, silvering o'er the stream
Of human thought with unabiding glory;
Not quite a waking truth, not quite a dream,
A visitation, bright and transitory.

But she is changed,—hath felt the touch of sorrow,
No love hath she, no understanding friend;
O grief! when Heaven is forced of earth to borrow
What the poor niggard earth has not to lend;
But when the stalk is snapped, the rose must bend.
The tallest flower that skyward rears its head
Grows from the common ground, and there must shed
Its delicate petals. Cruel fate, too surely,
That they should find so base a bridal bed,
Who lived in virgin pride, so sweet and purely.

She had a brother, and a tender father,
And she was loved, but not as others are
From whom we ask return of love,—but rather
As one might love a dream; a phantom fair
Of something exquisitely strange and rare,
Which all were glad to look on, men and maids,—

Yet no one claimed—as oft, in dewy glades,
The peering primrose, like sudden gladness,
Gleams on the soul, yet unregarded fades;—
The joy is ours, but all its own the sadness.

'Tis vain to say—her worst of grief is only
The common lot which all the world have known;
To her 'tis more, because her heart is lonely,
And yet she hath no strength to stand alone,—
Once she had playmates, fancies of her own,
And she did love them. They are passed away
As Fairies vanish at the break of day;
And like a spectre of an age departed,
Or unsphered Angel woefully astray,
She glides along—the solitary-hearted.

HARTLEY COLERIDGE

Auld Robin Gray

When the sheep are in the fauld, and the kye at hame,
And a' the warld to rest are gane,
The waes o' my heart fa' in showers frae my e'e,
While my gudeman lies sound by me.

Young Jamie lo'ed me weel, and sought me for his
    bride;
But saving a croun he had naething else beside:
To make the croun a pund, young Jamie gaed to sea;
And the croun and the pund were baith for me.

He hadna been awa' a week but only twa,
When my father brak his arm, and the kye was stown
    awa';
My mother she fell sick,—and my Jamie at the sea—
And auld Robin Gray came a-courtin' me.

My father couldna work, and my mother couldna spin;
I toiled day and night, but their bread I couldna win;
Auld Robin maintained them baith, and wi' tears in
    his e'e
Said, "Jennie, for their sakes, O, marry me!"

My heart it said nay; I looked for Jamie back;
But the wind it blew high, and the ship it was a wrack;
His ship it was a wrack— Why didna Jamie dee?
Or why do I live to cry, Wae's me!

My father urged me sore: my mother didna speak;
But she looked in my face till my heart was like t
    break:
They gi'ed him my hand, though my heart was in th
    sea;
Sae auld Robin Gray he was gudeman to me.

I hadna been a wife a week but only four,
When mournfu' as I sat on the stane at the door,
I saw my Jamie's wraith,—for I couldna think it he,
Till he said, "I'm come hame to marry thee."

O, sair, sair did we greet, and muckle did we say;
We took but ae kiss, and we tore ourselves away:
I wish that I were dead, but I'm no like to dee;
And why was I born to say, Wae's me!

I gang like a ghaist, and I carena to spin;
I daurna think on Jamie, for that wad be a sin;
But I'll do my best a gude wife aye to be,
For auld Robin Gray he is kind unto me.

ANNE BARNA

From the Hills, from the Roads, from the Sea

The Mountain Woman

Among the sullen peaks she stood at bay
And paid life's hard account from her small store.
Knowing the code of mountain wives, she bore
The burden of the days without a sigh;
And sharp against the somber winter sky,
I saw her drive her steers afield each day.

Hers was the hand that sunk the furrows deep
Across the rocky, grudging southern slope.
At first youth left her face, and later hope;
Yet through each mocking spring and barren fall,
She reared her lusty brood, and gave them all
That gladder wives and mothers love to keep.

And when the sheriff shot her eldest son
Beside his still, so well she knew her part,
She gave no healing tears to ease her heart;
But took the blow upstanding, with her eyes
As drear and bitter as the winter skies.
Seeing her then, I thought that she had won.

But yesterday her man returned too soon
And found her tending, with a reverent touch,
One scarlet bloom; and, having drunk too much,
He snatched its flame and quenched it in the dirt.
Then like a creature with a mortal hurt,
She fell, and wept away the afternoon.

DUBOSE HEYWARD

A Hill-Woman

You'd think I'd hate the hills?—well, this life brir
Little that's new. Once many years ago
I thought I'd leave the place and flee below,
Down where the world is bright with life and chan
But I met him, and now—it's very strange
How marriage changes things.

Listen!—beyond that grove (you would not knov
A hermit thrush, it sings round five each night!
One moment now, and *he* will come in sight
Driving the chestnut mare! There, that's his call!
I hate the hills? How could I now, at all,
Knowing he loves me so?

JOHN FARR

An Old Woman of the Roads

Oh, to have a little house!
  To own the hearth and stool and all!
The heaped-up sods upon the fire,
  The pile of turf against the wall!

To have a clock with weights and chains,
  And pendulum swinging up and down!
A dresser filled with shining delph,
  Speckled and white and blue and brown!

I could be busy all the day
  Clearing and sweeping hearth and floor,
And fixing on their shelf again
  My white and blue and speckled store!

I could be quiet there at night
  Beside the fire and by myself,
Sure of a bed and loth to leave
  The ticking clock and the shining delph!

Och! but I'm weary of mist and dark,
  And roads where there's never a house nor bush;
And tired I am of bog and road,
  And the crying wind and the lonesome hush!

And I am praying to God on high,
  And I am praying Him night and day,
For a little house—a house of my own—
  Out of the wind's and the rain's way.

PADRAIC COLUM

The Vagabonds

We are two travellers, Roger and I.
   Roger's my dog. —Come here, you scamp!
Jump for the gentleman,—mind your eye!
   Over the table,—look out for the lamp!
The rogue is growing a little old;
   Five years we've tramped through wind and weathe
And slept out-doors when nights were cold,
   And ate and drunk—and starved—together.

We've learned what comfort is, I tell you!
   A bed on the floor, a bit of rosin,
A fire to thaw our thumbs (poor fellow,
   The paw he holds up there's been frozen),
Plenty of catgut for my fiddle
   (This out-door business is bad for strings),
Then a few nice buckwheats hot from the griddle,
   And Roger and I set up for kings!

No, thank ye, Sir,—I never drink;
   Roger and I are exceedingly moral,—
Aren't we, Roger?—See him wink!—
   Well, something hot then,—we won't quarrel.
He's thirsty, too,—see him nod his head?
   What a pity, Sir, that dogs can't talk!
He understands every word that's said,—
   And he knows good milk from water-and-chalk.

The truth is, Sir, now I reflect,
    I've been so badly given to grog,
I wonder I've not lost the respect
    (Here's to you, Sir!) even of my dog.
But he sticks by, through thick and thin;
    And this old coat, with its empty pockets,
And rags that smell of tobacco and gin,
    He'll follow while he has eyes in his sockets.

There isn't another creature living
    Would do it, and prove through every disaster,
So fond, so faithful, and so forgiving,
    To such a miserable, thankless master!
No, Sir!—see him wag his tail and grin!
    By George! it makes my old eyes water!
That is, there's something in this gin
    That chokes a fellow. But no matter!

We'll have some music, if you're willing,
    And Roger (hem! what a plague a cough is, Sir!)
Shall march a little— Start, you villain!
    Paws up! Eyes front! Salute your officer!
'Bout face! Attention! Take your rifle!
    (Some dogs have arms, you see!) Now hold your
Cap while the gentlemen give a trifle,
    To aid a poor old patriot soldier!

March! Halt! Now show how the rebel shakes
    When he stands up to hear his sentence.

Now tell us how many drams it takes
    To honor a jolly new acquaintance.
Five yelps,—that's five; he's mighty knowing!
    The night's before us, fill the glasses!—
Quick, Sir! I'm ill,—my brain is going!—
    Some brandy,—thank you,—there!—it passes!

Why not reform? That's easily said;
    But I've gone through such wretched treatment,
Sometimes forgetting the taste of bread,
    And scarce remembering what meat meant,
That my poor stomach's past reform;
    And there are times when, mad with thinking,
I'd sell out heaven for something warm
    To prop a horrible inward sinking.

Is there a way to forget to think?
    At your age, Sir, home, fortune, friends,
A dear girl's love,—but I took to drink,—
    The same old story; you know how it ends.
If you could have seen these classic features,—
    You needn't laugh, Sir; they were not then
Such a burning libel on God's creatures:
    I was one of your handsome men!

If you had seen *her,* so fair and young,
    Whose head was happy on this breast!
If you could have heard the songs I sung
    When the wine went round, you wouldn't have guess

That ever I, Sir, should be straying
    From door to door, with fiddle and dog,
Ragged and penniless, and playing
    To you tonight for a glass of grog!

She's married since,—a parson's wife:
    'Twas better for her that we should part,—
Better the soberest, prosiest life
    Than a blasted home and a broken heart.
I have seen her? Once: I was weak and spent
    On the dusty road: a carriage stopped:
But little she dreamed, as on she went,
    Who kissed the coin that her fingers dropped!

You've set me talking, Sir; I'm sorry;
    It makes me wild to think of the change!
What do you care for a beggar's story?
    Is it amusing? You find it strange?
I had a mother so proud of me!
    'Twas well she died before. Do you know
If the happy spirits in heaven can see
    The ruin and wretchedness here below?

Another glass, and strong, to deaden
    This pain; then Roger and I will start.
I wonder, has he such a lumpish, leaden
    Aching thing, in place of a heart?
He is sad sometimes, and would weep, if he could,
    No doubt remembering things that were,—
A virtuous kennel with plenty of food,
    And himself a sober, respectable cur.

I'm better now; that glass was warming.—
    You rascal! limber your lazy feet!
We must be fiddling and performing
    For supper and bed, or starve in the street.
Not a very gay life we lead, you think?
    But soon we shall go where lodgings are free,
And the sleepers need neither victuals nor drink:—
    The sooner the better for Roger and me!

JOHN TOWNSEND TROWBRIDGE

Juggling Jerry

Pitch here the tent, while the old horse grazes:
　By the old hedge-side we'll halt a stage.
It's nigh my last above the daisies:
　My next leaf'll be man's blank page.
Yes, my old girl! and it's no use crying:
　Juggler, constable, king, must bow.
One that outjuggles all's been spying
　Long to have me, and he has me now.

We've travelled times to this old common:
　Often we've hung our pots in the gorse.
We've had a stirring life, old woman,
　You, and I, and the old grey horse.
Races, and fairs, and royal occasions,
　Found us coming to their call:
Now they'll miss us at our stations:
　There's a Juggler outjuggles all!

Up goes the lark, as if all were jolly!
　Over the duck-pond the willow shakes.
Easy to think that grieving's folly,
　When the hand's firm as driven stakes!
Ay, when we're strong, and braced, and manful,
　Life's a sweet fiddle: but we're a batch
Born to become the Great Juggler's han'ful:
　Balls he shies up, and is safe to catch.

Here's where the lads of the village cricket:
    I was a lad not wide from here:
Couldn't I whip off the bail from the wicket?
    Like an old world those days appear!
Donkey, sheep, geese, and thatched ale-house—I know
    them!
    They are old friends of my haunts, and seem,
Somehow, as if kind thanks I owe them:
    Juggling don't hinder the heart's esteem.

Juggling's no sin, for we must have victual:
    Nature allows us to bait for the fool.
Holding one's own makes us juggle no little;
    But, to increase it, hard juggling's the rule.
You that are sneering at my profession,
    Haven't you juggled a vast amount?
There's the Prime Minister, in one Session,
    Juggles more games than my sins'll count.

I've murdered insects with mock thunder:
    Conscience, for that, in men don't quail.
I've made bread from the bump of wonder:
    That's my business, and there's my tale.
Fashion and rank all praised the professor:
    Ay! and I've had my smile from the Queen:
Bravo, Jerry! she meant: God bless her!
    Ain't this a sermon on that scene?

I've studied men from my topsy-turvy
    Close, and, I reckon, rather true.
Some are fine fellows: some, right scurvy:
    Most, a dash between the two.

But it's a woman, old girl, that makes me
    Think more kindly of the race:
And it's a woman, old girl, that shakes me
    When the Great Juggler I must face.

We two were married, due and legal:
    Honest we've lived since we've been one.
Lord! I could jump then like an eagle:
    You danced bright as a bit o' the sun.
Birds in a May-bush we were! right merry!
    All night we kissed, we juggled all day.
Joy was the heart of Juggling Jerry!
    Now from his old girl he's juggled away.

It's past parsons to console us:
    No, nor no doctor fetch for me:
I can die without my bolus;
    Two of a trade, lass, never agree!
Parson and Doctor!—don't they love rarely
    Fighting the devil in other men's fields!
Stand up yourself and match him fairly:
    Then see how the rascal yields!

I, lass, have lived no gipsy, flaunting
    Finery while his poor helpmate grubs:
Coin I've stored, and you won't be wanting:
    You shan't beg from the troughs and tubs.
Nobly you've stuck to me, though in his kitchen
    Many a Marquis would hail you Cook!
Palaces you could have ruled and grown rich in,
    But your old Jerry you never forsook.

Hand up the chirper! ripe ale winks in it;
    Let's have comfort and be at peace.
Once a stout draught made me light as a linnet.
    Cheer up! the Lord must have his lease.
May be—for none see in that black hollow—
    It's just a place where we're held in pawn,
And when the Great Juggler makes as to swallow,
    It's just the sword-trick—I ain't quite gone!

Yonder came smells of the gorse, so nutty,
    Gold-like and warm: it's the prime of May.
Better than mortar, brick and putty,
    Is God's house on a blowing day.
Lean me more up the mound; now I feel it:
    All the old heath-smells! Ain't it strange?
There's the world laughing, as if to conceal it,
    But He's by us, juggling the change.

I mind it well, by the sea-beach lying,
    Once—it's long gone—when two gulls we beheld,
Which, as the moon got up, were flying
    Down a big wave that sparkled and swelled.
Crack, went a gun: one fell: the second
    Wheeled round him twice, and was off for new luck:
There in the dark her white wing beckoned:—
    Drop me a kiss—I'm the bird dead-struck!

GEORGE MEREDITH

John Popham

John Popham had a face like leather,
His sunburnt eyebrows came together,
His hair, that should have been pure white,
Was scorched to cornsilk by the light
Of fierce, windy Foreside suns,
His voice was deep down like far guns.
Seventy winters of stiff blows
Had built his face into a rose,
The bright salt sparkled in his blood,
His eyes were like a bay at flood
With sun-diamonds on it flowing.
John Popham was one very knowing
In the ways of wind and tide,
The weather had been his hard bride
Since he had put his legs inside
His first long trousers, dark and trim,
She'd made a long, strong man of him,
She had made him like blue steel
From his bronze prow to his keel,
She had made his thick thighs seasoned
Oak that was alive and reasoned;
His hands were like a pair of anchors.
All man's hungers and man's hankers
He had turned upon the calling
Of setting mackerel nets and trawling,
Of taking lobsters from the dark
Ocean floor. John's life was stark
Loneliness and the morning star

Flickering out at dawn, and tar,
Kelp and cordage, clean, sharp smells,
The tolling of the lonely bells
That mark the reefs below the brine
Where death humps up his jagged spine.
John's pockets were stuffed out with spears
Of white-pine plugs to wedge the shears
Of the dark green lobster claws.
John's life depended on the laws
Of moon-changes, flood and ebb,
The planets' paths, the subtle web
Of winds spread out to the twelve corners
Of the world, the bleak bull-horners
From the north, the crying south
With death and white bones in her mouth.
He had toed the mark between
Life and death, and toed it clean,
Kept six quarts of red blood warm
In square miles of brine and storm.
John kept away from other men,
In all there might have been some ten
He spoke to much, year in, year out.
He found his lonely way about
Shoals and blows and low-ebb hours.
His roof defied the gale's best powers
On an island bare and granite,
The sou'west surf could nearly span it,
It was the last one out of all,
Its white sides went down like a wall
Into dark water, swum by cod.
The man's wide hands were his sole God;

He could never long abide
Beach or mud exposed by tide,
He loved bold water at his door,
Being lonely, and the roar
Of the ocean, wave on wave,
That some fine day would be his grave.

ROBERT P. TRISTRAM COFFIN

A Dutch Picture

Simon Danz has come home again,
　　From cruising about with his buccaneers;
He has singed the beard of the King of Spain,
And carried away the Dean of Jaen
　　And sold him in Algiers.

In his house by the Maese, with its roof of tiles,
　　And weathercocks flying aloft in air,
There are silver tankards of antique styles,
Plunder of convent and castle, and piles
　　Of carpets rich and rare.

In his tulip-garden there by the town,
　　Overlooking the sluggish stream,
With his Moorish cap and dressing-gown,
The old sea-captain, hale and brown,
　　Walks in a waking dream.

A smile in his gray mustachio lurks
　　Whenever he thinks of the King of Spain,
And the listed tulips look like Turks,
And the silent gardener as he works
　　Is changed to the Dean of Jaen.

The windmills on the outermost
　　Verge of the landscape in the haze,
To him are towers on the Spanish coast,

With whiskered sentinels at their post,
  Though this is the river Maese.

But when the winter rains begin,
  He sits and smokes by the blazing brands,
And old seafaring men come in,
Goat-bearded, gray, and with double chin,
  And rings upon their hands.

They sit there in the shadow and shine
  Of the flickering fire of the winter night;
Figures in color and design
Like those by Rembrandt of the Rhine,
  Half darkness and half light.

And they talk of ventures lost or won,
  And their talk is ever and ever the same,
While they drink the red wine of Tarragon,
From the cellars of some Spanish Don,
  Or convent set on flame.

Restless at times with heavy strides
  He paces his parlor to and fro;
He is like a ship that at anchor rides,
And swings with the rising and falling tides,
  And tugs at her anchor-tow.

Voices mysterious far and near,
  Sound of the wind and sound of the sea,
Are calling and whispering in his ear,

"Simon Danz! Why stayest thou here?
   Come forth and follow me!"

So he thinks he shall take to the sea again
   For one more cruise with his buccaneers,
To singe the beard of the King of Spain,
And capture another Dean of Jaen
   And sell him in Algiers.

HENRY WADSWORTH LONGFELLOW

Captain Stratton's Fancy

Oh some are fond of red wine, and some are fond of white,
And some are all for dancing by the pale moonlight;
But rum alone's the tipple, and the heart's delight
    Of the old bold mate of Henry Morgan.

Oh some are fond of Spanish wine, and some are fond of
        French,
And some'll swallow tay and stuff fit only for a wench;
But I'm for ripe Jamaica till I roll beneath the bench,
    Says the old bold mate of Henry Morgan.

Oh some are for the lily, and some are for the rose,
But I am for the sugar-cane that in Jamaica grows;
For it's that that makes the bonny drink to warm my cop-
        per nose,
    Says the old bold mate of Henry Morgan.

Oh some are fond of fiddles, and a song well sung,
And some are all for music for to lilt upon the tongue;
But mouths were made for tankards, and for sucking at the
        bung,
    Says the old bold mate of Henry Morgan.

Oh some are fond of dancing, and some are fond of dice,
And some are all for red lips, and pretty lasses' eyes;
But a right Jamaica puncheon is a finer prize
    To the old bold mate of Henry Morgan.

Oh some that's good and godly ones they hold that it's a sin
To troll the jolly bowl around, and let the dollars spin;
But I'm for toleration and for drinking at an inn,
     Says the old bold mate of Henry Morgan.

Oh some are sad and wretched folk that go in silken suits
And there's a mort of wicked rogues that live in good re
          putes;
So I'm for drinking honestly, and dying in my boots,
     Like an old bold mate of Henry Morgan.

JOHN MASEFIELD

"All
That's
Past"

Old Grimes

Old Grimes is dead; that good old man
    We never shall see more:
He used to wear a long black coat,
    All buttoned down before.

His heart was open as the day,
    His feelings all were true;
His hair was some inclined to gray—
    He wore it in a queue.

Whene'er he heard the voice of pain,
    His breast with pity burned;
The large, round head upon his cane
    From ivory was turned.

Kind words he had for all;
    He knew no base design:
His eyes were dark and rather small,
    His nose was aquiline.

He lived at peace with all mankind,
    In friendship he was true;
His coat had pocket-holes behind,
    His pantaloons were blue.

Unharmed, the sin which earth pollutes
    He passed securely o'er,
And never wore a pair of boots
    For thirty years or more.

But good old Grimes is now at rest,
  Nor fears misfortune's frown:
He wore a double-breasted vest—
  The stripes ran up and down.

He modest merit sought to find,
  And pay it its desert:
He had no malice in his mind,
  No ruffles on his shirt.

His neighbors he did not abuse—
  Was sociable and gay:
He wore large buckles on his shoes,
  And changed them every day.

His knowledge, hid from public gaze,
  He did not bring to view,
Nor made a noise, town-meeting days,
  As many people do.

His worldly goods he never threw
  In trust to fortune's chances,
But lived (as all his brothers do)
  In easy circumstances.

Thus undisturbed by anxious cares,
  His peaceful moments ran;
And everybody said he was
  A fine old gentleman.

ALBERT GORTON GREENE

The Last Leaf

I saw him once before,
As he passed by the door,
    And again
The pavement stones resound
As he totters o'er the ground
    With his cane.

They say that in his prime,
Ere the pruning-knife of Time
    Cut him down,
Not a better man was found
By the crier on his round
    Through the town.

But now he walks the streets,
And he looks at all he meets
    Sad and wan,
And he shakes his feeble head,
That it seems as if he said,
    "They are gone."

The mossy marbles rest
On the lips that he has pressed
    In their bloom,
And the names he loved to hear
Have been carved for many a year
    On the tomb.

My grandmamma has said—
Poor old lady, she is dead
    Long ago—
That he had a Roman nose,
And his cheek was like a rose
    In the snow.

But now his nose is thin,
And it rests upon his chin
    Like a staff,
And a crook is in his back,
And a melancholy crack
    In his laugh.

I know it is a sin
For me to sit and grin
    At him here;
But the old three-cornered hat,
And the breeches, and all that,
    Are so queer!

And if I should live to be
The last leaf upon the tree
    In the spring,
Let them smile, as I do now,
At the old forsaken bough
    Where I cling.

OLIVER WENDELL HOLMES

Old John Henry

Old John's jes' made o' the commonest stuff—
          Old John Henry—
He's tough, I reckon,—but none too tough—
Too tough though's better than not enough!
          Says old John Henry.
He does his best, and when his best's bad,
He don't fret none, ner he don't git sad—
He simply 'lows it's the best he had:
          Old John Henry—

His doctern's jes' o' the plainest brand—
          Old John Henry—
A smilin' face and a hearty hand
'S religen 'at all folks understand,
          Says old John Henry.
He's stove up some with the rhumatiz,
And they hain't no shine on them shoes o' his,
And his hair hain't cut—but his eye-teeth is:
          Old John Henry!

He feeds hiss'f when the stock's all fed—
          Old John Henry—
And sleeps like a babe when he goes to bed—
And dreams o' heaven and home-made bread,
          Says old John Henry.
He hain't refined as he'd ort to be
To fit the statutes o' poetry,
Ner his clothes don't fit him—but *he* fits *me:*
          Old John Henry.

JAMES WHITCOMB RILEY

An Old Man's Winter Night

All out-of-doors looked darkly in at him
Through the thin frost, almost in separate stars,
That gathers on the pane in empty rooms.
What kept his eyes from giving back the gaze
Was the lamp tilted near them in his hand.
What kept him from remembering what it was
That brought him to that creaking room was age.
He stood with barrels round him—at a loss;
And having scared the cellar under him
In clomping there, he scared it once again
In clomping off; and scared the outer night,
Which has its sounds, familiar, like the roar
Of trees and crack of branches—common things,
But nothing so like beating on a box.
A light he was to no one but himself
Where now he sat, concerned with he knew what;
A quiet light, and then not even that.
He consigned to the moon, such as she was,
So late-arising, to the broken moon—
As better than the sun in any case
For such a charge—his snow upon the roof,
His icicles along the wall to keep;
And slept. The log that shifted with a jolt
Once in the stove, disturbed him and he shifted,
And eased his heavy breathing; but still slept.
One aged man—one man—can't fill a house,
A farm, a countryside; or if he can,
It's thus he does it of a winter night.

ROBERT FROST

Old Susan

When Susan's work was done, she'd sit,
With one fat guttering candle lit,
And window opened wide to win
The sweet night air to enter in.
There, with a thumb to keep her place,
She'd read, with stern and wrinkled face,
Her mild eyes gliding very slow
Across the letters to and fro,
While wagged the guttering candle-flame
In the wind that through the window came.
And sometimes in the silence she
Would mumble a sentence audibly,
Or shake her head as if to say,
"You silly souls, to act this way!"
And never a sound from night I would hear,
Unless some far-off cock crowed clear;
Or her old shuffling thumb should turn
Another page; and rapt and stern,
Through her great glasses bent on me,
She'd glance into reality;
And shake her round old silvery head,
With—"You!—I thought you was in bed!"—
Only to tilt her book again,
And rooted in Romance remain.

WALTER DE LA MARE

Mary O'Brian

Mary O'Brian is old and she wears a black shawl,
Black against the grey grass and the grey hill beyond,
Black in the fading day on the pale cottage wall,
And she drives three cows with a bent hazel wand;
Three black cows, and they walk in a row
From the day's green pasture to the night's black stall,
With slowly swaying heads and feet moving slow.

And she will sit in the dusk by the red turf embers,
With her weary eyes fixed on the last faint glow,
And she will see again the faces she remembers,
And think of the summers that were hers long ago;
And she will start a little and draw her shawl close
As the old faces fade and the chill of life's Novembers
Stirs the dry leaves of love's flowerless rose.

And when the hearth is black and the night has filled th
    room,
And the night-wind has risen and the sound of the ebb-tid
    grows
Into a great voice that whispers in the gloom,
Still she sits in the silence—and no man knows
What sad long thoughts, what hopes and what despairs,
She stretches like a warp on her spirit's dark loom
To weave herself a garment with the shuttle of her prayer

J. REDWOOD ANDERSO

The Old Lady

The old, old lady,
that nobody knows,
sits in the Garden
shelter, and sews.

Save for her restless
fingers she
is cold and still
as ivory.

The chestnut-blossom,
blown on her dress,
seems only a sculptor's
cleverness.

HUMBERT WOLFE

The Fine Old English Gentleman

I'll sing you a good old song,
  Made by a good old pate,
Of a fine old English gentleman
  Who had an old estate,
And who kept up his old mansion
  At a bountiful old rate;
With a good old porter to relieve
  The old poor at his gate,
Like a fine old English gentleman
  All of the olden time.

His hall so old was hung around
  With pikes and guns and bows,
And swords, and good old bucklers,
  That had stood some tough old blows;
'Twas there "his worship" held his state
  In doublet and trunk hose,
And quaffed his cup of good old sack,
  To warm his good old nose,
Like a fine old English gentleman
  All of the olden time.

When winter's cold brought frost and snow,
  He opened house to all;
And though threescore and ten his years,
  He featly led the ball;
Nor was the houseless wanderer
  E'er driven from his hall;

For while he feasted all the great,
    He ne'er forgot the small;
Like a fine old English gentleman
    All of the olden time.

But time, though old, is strong in flight,
    And years rolled swiftly by;
And Autumn's falling leaves proclaimed
    This good old man must die!
He laid him down right tranquilly,
    Gave up life's latest sigh;
And mournful stillness reigned around,
    And tears bedewed each eye,
For this fine old English gentleman
    All of the olden time.

Now surely this is better far
    Than all the new parade
Of theaters and fancy balls
    "At home" and masquerade:
And much more economical,
    For all his bills were paid.
Then leave your new vagaries quite,
    And take up the old trade
Of a fine old English gentleman,
    All of the olden time.

ANONYMOUS

People
from
History

Caesar Remembers

Caesar, that proud man,
   Sat in his tent,
Weary with victory,
   With striving spent.

Where the grey Chilterns
   Coiled and slept
That hard-lipped Emperor
   Vigil kept.

In the thin starlight
   His glimmering hordes
Fought with the hard earth—
   Spades for swords.

Out on the hill-slopes
   His helmèd host
Piled stark ramparts
   Rimmed with frost.

But Caesar cared not
   For dyke and wall,
Faint and remote
   Came the bugles' call;

Soft in the shadows
   He saw, and heard,
A Roman garden,
   A Roman bird.

"Worlds to conquer!
    But Caesar fails
To add one song
    To the nightingale's!"

Soft in the shadows
    The tired man heard
A woman's laughter,
    A woman's word.

Caesar, shivering,
    Heard repeat
Spades on the hillside,
    Sentries' feet.

WILLIAM KEAN SEYMOUR

124

Antony to Cleopatra

I am dying, Egypt, dying!
  Ebbs the crimson life-tide fast,
And the dark Plutonian shadows
  Gather on the evening blast;
Let thine arm, O Queen, enfold me,
  Hush thy sobs and bow thine ear,
Listen to the great heart secrets
  Thou, and thou alone, must hear.

Though my scarred and veteran legions
  Bear their eagles high no more,
And my wrecked and scattered galleys
  Strew dark Actium's fatal shore;
Though no glittering guards surround me,
  Prompt to do their master's will,
I must perish like a Roman,
  Die the great Triumvir still.

Let not Caesar's servile minions
  Mock the lion thus laid low;
'Twas no foeman's arm that felled him,
  'Twas his own that struck the blow:
His who, pillowed on thy bosom,
  Turned aside from glory's ray—
His who, drunk with thy caresses,
  Madly threw a world away.

Should the base plebian rabble
    Dare assail my name at Rome,
Where the noble spouse Octavia
    Weeps within her widowed home,
Seek her; say the gods bear witness,—
    Altars, augurs, circling wings,—
That her blood, with mine commingled,
    Yet shall mount the thrones of kings.

And for thee, star-eyed Egyptian—
    Glorious sorceress of the Nile!
Light the path to Stygian horrors,
    With the splendor of thy smile;
Give the Caesar crowns and arches,
    Let his brow the laurel twine:
I can scorn the senate's triumphs,
    Triumphing in love like thine.

I am dying, Egypt, dying!
    Hark! the insulting foeman's cry;
They are coming—quick, my falchion!
    Let them front me ere I die.
Ah, no more amid the battle
    Shall my heart exulting swell;
Isis and Osiris guard thee—
    Cleopatra—Rome—farewell!

WILLIAM HAINES LYTLE

Saint John Baptist

The last and greatest herald of heaven's King
Girt with rough skins, hies to the deserts wild,
Among that savage brood the woods forth bring,
Which he more harmless found than man, and mild.
His food was locusts, and what there doth spring,
With honey that from virgin hives distilled;
Parched body, hollow eyes, some uncouth thing
Made him appear, long since from earth exiled.
There burst he forth: All ye whose hopes rely
On God, with me amidst these deserts mourn,
Repent, repent, and from old errors turn!
—Who listened to his voice, obeyed his cry?
Only the echoes, which he made relent,
Rung from their flinty caves, Repent! Repent!

WILLIAM   DRUMMOND

Chaucer

An old man in a lodge within a park;
The chamber walls depicted all around
With portraitures of huntsman, hawk, and hound,
And the hurt deer. He listeneth to the lark,
Whose song comes with the sunshine through the da
Of painted glass in leaden lattice bound;
He listeneth and he laugheth at the sound,
Then writeth in a book like any clerk.
He is the poet of the dawn, who wrote
The Canterbury Tales, and his old age
Made beautiful with song; and as I read
I hear the crowing cock, I hear the note
Of lark and linnet, and from every page
Rise odors of plowed field or flowery mead.

HENRY WADSWORTH LONGFELLO

There Lived a Lady in Milan

There lived a lady in Milan
Wrought for a madness unto Man,
A fawn Il Moro could not tame;
Her beauty unbedecked with pearls
More than all Beatrice's girls,
Her eyes a subtle flame.

Brocade wherein her body dressed
Was hallowed; flowers her footstep pressed
Suspired incense ere they died.
Her father mazed with alchemy
Wrought in his cellar ceaselessly.
She lived in quiet, gentle pride.

And by her garden in his hour
Passed Leonardo, come with power
From Florence. So he saw her face
Bending above the shrivelled stalks
Of autumn on the garden walks.
And Leonardo drank her grace.

She was as if a sunset were
With fresher colors, clearer air,
And a more golden coil of cloud.
She was as if all citherns swooned
With one rich harmony myriad-tuned,
Haunting, enchanting, pure and proud.

And Leonardo said, "Ladye,
I know not what you do to me
Who have and have not, seek nor find.
The sea-shell and the falcon's feather,
Greece and the rock and shifting weather
Have taught me many things of mind.

"My heart has taught me many things,
And so have emperors, popes, and kings,
And so have leaves and green May-flies;
Yea, I have learned from bird and beast,
From slouching dwarf and ranting priest.
Yet, in the end, how am I wise?

"Though with dividers and a quill
I weave some miracle of will,—
Say, that men fly,—though I design
For peace or war a thousand things
Gaining applause from dukes and kings,—
Though soft and deft my colors shine,

"Though my quick wit breeds thunderbolts
I may not loose on all these dolts,
Things they are babes to comprehend,—
Though from the crevice in stone or lime
I trace grave outlines mocking Time,—
I know when I am beaten, Friend!

"Say that there lived of old a saint
Even Leonardo dared not paint,
Even Leonardo dared not draw,—

Too perfect in her breathing prime
For colors to transmit to time
Or quill attempt,—aye, ev'n in awe!

"Say this, cold histories, and say
I looked not on her from this day
Lest frenzied I destroy my art.
O golden lily,—how she stands
Listening! Beauty,—ah, your hands,
Your little hands tear out my heart!

"Do you not know you are so fair,
Brighter than springtime in the air?
What says your mirror to your mind?"
"Phantom," she whispered, "Do you plead
With ghostly gestures? . . . Ah, indeed,
Pity a lady deaf and blind

"Since birth!" . . . Then Leonardo turned
Saluting, though the sunset burned
In nimbus round her,—went his way
In daze, repeating "God's defect,
Even he!—and masterpiece elect!"
He never saw her from that day.

WILLIAM ROSE BENÉT

Henry VIII

Bluff King Hal was full of beans;
He married half a dozen queens;
For three called Kate they cried the bans,
And one called Jane, and a couple of Annes.

The first he asked to share his reign
Was Kate of Aragon, straight from Spain—
But when his love for her was spent,
He got a divorce, and out she went.

Anne Boleyn was his second wife;
He swore to cherish her all his life—
But seeing a third he wished instead,
He chopped off poor Anne Boleyn's head.

He married the next afternoon
Jane Seymour, which was rather soon—
But after one year as his bride
She crept into her bed and died.

Anne of Cleves was Number Four;
Her portrait thrilled him to the core—
But when he met her face to face
Another royal divorce took place.

Catherine Howard, Number Five,
Billed and cooed to keep alive—
But one day Henry felt depressed;
The executioner did the rest.

Sixth and last came Catherine Parr,
Sixth and last and luckiest far—
For this time it was Henry who
Hopped the twig, and a good job too.

ELEANOR AND HERBERT FARJEON

The Looking-Glass

Queen Bess was Harry's daughter. Stand forward partner
    all!
In ruff and stomacher and gown
She danced King Philip down-a-down,
And left her shoe to show 'twas true—
    (*The very tune I'm playing you*)
In Norgem at Brickwall!

The Queen was in her chamber, and she was middling old.
Her petticoat was satin, and her stomacher was gold.
Backwards and forwards and sideways did she pass,
Making up her mind to face the cruel looking-glass.
The cruel looking-glass that will never show a lass
As comely or as kindly or as young as what she was!

Queen Bess was Harry's daughter. Now hand your partner
    all!

The Queen was in her chamber, a-combing of her hair.
There came Queen Mary's spirit and It stood behind her
    chair,
Singing "Backwards and forwards and sideways may you
    pass,
But I will stand behind you till you face the looking-glass,
The cruel looking-glass that will never show a lass
As lovely or unlucky or as lonely as I was!"

*ueen Bess was Harry's daughter. Now turn your partners
   all!*

he Queen was in her chamber, a-weeping very sore,
here came Lord Leicester's spirit and It scratched upon the
   door,
nging "Backwards and forwards and sideways may you
   pass,
ut I will walk beside you till you face the looking-glass.
he cruel looking-glass that will never show a lass,
; hard and unforgiving or as wicked as you was!"

*ueen Bess was Harry's daughter. Now kiss your partners
   all!*

he Queen was in her chamber, her sins were on her head.
ie looked the spirits up and down and statelily she said:—
Backwards and forwards and sideways though I've been,
et I am Harry's daughter and I am England's Queen!"
id she faced the looking-glass (and whatever else there
   was)
id she saw her day was over and she saw her beauty pass
 the cruel looking-glass, that can always hurt a lass
ore hard than any ghost there is or any man there was!

RUDYARD KIPLING

135

Sir Philip Sidney

Here blooms the flower
Of Bess's Court,
Whose unstain'd hour
On earth was short.

Of courtesy
He was the prince,
None such as he
Before or since.

He held his cause
In honor's name,
His temper was
A shining flame.

With pen and sword,
In dance and fight,
A lovely lord,
A perfect knight.

On Zutphen's field
By mortal wound
His fate was sealed.
For thirst he swooned.

One ran, and brought
A brimming cup;
But ere he sought
The first sweet sup,

He caught a poor
Man's fevered eye,
Who at death's door
Did near him lie.

Amid the slaughter
Where they bled,
'Take him the water,'
Sidney said—

(The water, sweeter
Then than wine)—
'His need is greater
Yet than mine.'

Crowning his dower
Of high report,
Thus died the flower
Of Bess's Court.

He wrote sweet prose
And sweeter song.
So bright a rose
Could not live long.

ELEANOR AND HERBERT FARJEON

On the Death of Marie, Countess of Pembroke

Underneath this marble hearse
Lies the subject of all verse:
Sidney's sister, Pembroke's mother:
Death, ere thou hast killed another,
Fair, and learn'd, and good as she,
Time shall throw a dart at thee.

Marble piles let no man raise
To her name, for after days;
Some kind woman born as she
Reading this, like Niobe,
Shall turn marble, and become
Both her mourner and her tomb.

WILLIAM   BROWNE

Epitaph on Charles II

Here lies our Sovereign Lord the King,
   Whose word no man relies on,
Who never said a foolish thing,
   Nor ever did a wise one.

JOHN WILMOT, EARL OF ROCHESTER

Rob Roy

Rob Roy Macgregor
Could fling a fine reel,
    Och! aye!
With toe and with heel,
And skirl on the bagpipes
Beyond any man,
And was merry and lawless
And loved by his clan!

Rob Roy Macgregor
Stole cattle and sheep,
    Och! aye!
When folk were asleep,
Driving other men's cows
To his lair from the farm,
With other men's lambkins
Tucked under his arm!

Rob Roy Macgregor
Kept robbing the Roy,
    Och! aye!
With Jacobite joy!
He helped all his friends,
And he cursed all his foes,
Crying, 'Down with the King
And the Duke of Montrose!'

Rob Roy Macgregor
Was partial to loot,
    Och! aye!
And a rebel to boot!
His heart it was good,
If the ways they were bad,
Of Rob Roy Macgregor,
That daredevil lad!

ELEANOR AND HERBERT FARJEON

"I Am Monarch of All I Survey"

Supposed to be written by Alexander Selkirk, during his so
tary abode in the island of Juan Fernández

I am monarch of all I survey,
   My right there is none to dispute;
From the centre all round to the sea,
   I am lord of the fowl and the brute.
Oh, solitude! where are the charms
   That sages have seen in thy face?
Better dwell in the midst of alarms,
   Than reign in this horrible place.

I am out of humanity's reach,
   I must finish my journey alone,
Never hear the sweet music of speech;
   I start at the sound of my own.
The beasts, that roam over the plain,
   My form with indifference see;
They are so unacquainted with man,
   Their tameness is shocking to me.

Society, friendship, and love,
   Divinely bestow'd upon man,
Oh, had I the wings of a dove,
   How soon would I taste you again!
My sorrows I then might assuage
   In the ways of religion and truth,
Might learn from the wisdom of age,
   And be cheer'd by the sallies of youth.

Religion! what treasure untold
    Resides in that heavenly word!
More precious than silver and gold,
    Or all that this earth can afford.
But the sound of the church-going bell
    These valleys and rocks never heard,
Ne'er sigh'd at the sound of a knell,
    Or smil'd when a sabbath appear'd.

Ye winds, that have made me your sport,
    Convey to this desolate shore
Some cordial endearing report
    Of a land I shall visit no more.
My friends, do they now and then send
    A wish or a thought after me?
O tell me I yet have a friend,
    Though a friend I am never to see.

How fleet is a glance of the mind!
    Compar'd with the speed of its flight,
The tempest itself lags behind,
    And the swift wing'd arrows of light.
When I think of my own native land,
    In a moment I seem to be there;
But alas! recollection at hand
    Soon hurries me back to despair.

But the sea-fowl is gone to her nest,
    The beast is laid down in his lair,
Ev'n here is a season of rest,
    And I to my cabin repair.

There is mercy in every place;
　And mercy, encouraging thought!
Gives even affliction a grace,
　And reconciles man to his lot.

WILLIAM COWPER

Lincoln, the Man of the People

When the Norn Mother saw the Whirlwind Hour
Greatening and darkening as it hurried on,
She left the Heaven of Heroes and came down
To make a man to meet the mortal need.
She took the tried clay of the common road—
Clay warm yet with the ancient heat of Earth,
Dashed through it all a strain of prophecy;
Tempered the heap with thrill of human tears;
Then mixed a laughter with the serious stuff.
Into the shape she breathed a flame to light
That tender, tragic, ever-changing face.
Here was a man to hold against the world,
A man to match the mountains and the sea.

The color of the ground was in him, the red earth;
The smell and smack of elemental things:
The rectitude and patience of the cliff;
The good-will of the rain that loves all leaves;
The friendly welcome of the wayside well;
The courage of the bird that dares the sea;
The gladness of the wind that shakes the corn;
The mercy of the snow that hides all scars;
The secrecy of streams that make their way
Beneath the mountain to the rifted rock;
The undelaying justice of the light
That gives as freely to the shrinking flower
As to the great oak flaring to the wind—
To the grave's low hill as to the Matterhorn
That shoulders out the sky.

Sprung from the West
The strength of virgin forests braced his mind,
The hush of spacious prairies stilled his soul.
Up from log cabin to the Capitol,
One fire was on his spirit, one resolve—
To send the keen ax to the root of wrong,
Clearing a free way for the feet of God.
And evermore he burned to do his deed
With the fine stroke and gesture of a king:
He built the rail-pile as he built the State,
Pouring his splendid strength through every blow,
The conscience of him testing every stroke,
To make his deed the measure of a man.

So came the Captain with the thinking heart;
And when the judgment thunders split the house,
Wrenching the rafters from their ancient rest,
He held the ridgepole up, and spiked again
The rafters of the Home. He held his place—
Held the long purpose like a growing tree—
Held on through blame and faltered not at praise.
And when he fell in whirlwind, he went down
As when a lordly cedar, green with boughs,
Goes down with a great shout upon the hills,
And leaves a lonesome place against the sky.

EDWIN MARKHAM

Abraham Lincoln Walks at Midnight

In Springfield, Illinois

It is portentous, and a thing of state
That here at midnight in our little town,
A mourning figure walks, and will not rest,
Near the old court-house pacing up and down.

Or by his homestead, or in shadowed yards,
He lingers where his children used to play;
Or through the market, on the well-worn stones,
He stalks until the dawn-stars burn away.

A bronzed lank man! His suit of ancient black,
A famous high top-hat and plain worn shawl,
Make his the quaint great figure that men love,
The prairie lawyer, master of us all.

He cannot sleep upon the hillside now.
He is among us—as in times before!
And we who toss and lie awake for long
Breathe deep, and start, to see him pass the door.

His head is bowed. He thinks on men and kings.
Yes, when the sick world cries, how can he sleep?
Too many peasants fight, they know not why;
Too many homesteads in black terror weep.

The sins of all the war-lords burn his heart.
He sees the dreadnoughts scouring every main.

He carries on his shawl-wrapped shoulders now
The bitterness, the folly and the pain.

He cannot rest until a spirit-dawn
Shall come—the shining hope of Europe free:
The league of sober folk, the Workers' Earth,
Bringing long peace to Cornland, Alp and Sea.

It breaks his heart that kings must murder still,
That all his hours of travail here for men
Seem yet in vain. And who will bring white peace
That he may sleep upon his hill again?

VACHEL LINDSAY

The Queen in Parliament, 1941

(Queen Elizabeth, the Queen Mother)

I cannot say why—
But the Queen made me cry.

She sat by the King,
She said not a thing:
She said not a word,
But every heart stirred.
His job was not fun,
But the job was well done.
He did it alone—
But *she* sat by the throne.
Then he gave her his arm—
Grace, dignity, charm,
And a spirit so rare
There was joy in the air.
She curtsied, she smiled,
Like a queen—like a child.
She said not a word,
But every heart stirred;
And when they withdrew
Every heart went out too.
The King, with his men,
Opened Parliament then:
But the Queen opened more—
British women at war.

I think I know why
The Queen made me cry.

A. P. HERBERT

Shakespeare

Others abide our question. Thou art free.
We ask and ask— Thou smilest and art still,
Out-topping knowledge. For the loftiest hill,
Who to the stars uncrowns his majesty,
Planting his steadfast footsteps in the sea,
Making the heaven of heavens his dwelling-place,
Spares but the cloudy border of his base
To the foiled searching of mortality;
And thou, who didst the stars and sunbeams know,
Self-schooled, self-scanned, self-honored, self-secure,
Didst tread on earth unguessed at.—Better so!
All pains the immortal spirit must endure,
All weakness which impairs, all griefs which bow,
Find their sole speech in that victorious brow.

MATTHEW ARNOLD

Farragut

(Mobile Bay, August 5, 1864)

Farragut, Farragut,
   Old Heart of Oak,
Daring Dave Farragut,
   Thunderbolt stroke,
Watches the hoary mist
   Lift from the bay,
Till his flag, glory-kissed,
   Greets the young day.

Far, by gray Morgan's walls,
   Looms the black fleet.
Hark, deck to rampart calls
   With the drums' beat!
Buoy your chains overboard,
   While the steam hums;
Men! to the battlement,
   Farragut comes.

See, as the hurricane
   Hurtles in wrath
Squadrons of clouds amain
   Back from its path!
Back to the parapet,
   To the guns' lips,
Thunderbolt Farragut
   Hurls the black ships.

Now through the battle's roar
 Clear the boy sings,
"By the mark fathoms four,"
 While his lead swings.
Steady the wheelmen five
 "Nor' by East keep her,"
"Steady," but two alive:
 How the shells sweep her!

Lashed to the mast that sways
 Over red decks,
Over the flame that plays
 Round the torn wrecks,
Over the dying lips
 Framed for a cheer,
Farragut leads his ships,
 Guides the line clear.

On by heights cannon-browed,
 While the spars quiver;
Onward still flames the cloud
 Where the hulks shiver.
See, yon fort's star is set,
 Storm and fire past.
Cheer him, lads—Farragut,
 Lashed to the mast!

Oh! while Atlantic's breast
 Bears a white sail,
While the Gull's towering crest
 Tops a green vale,

Men thy bold deeds shall tell,
Old Heart of Oak,
Daring Dave Farragut,
Thunderbolt stroke!

WILLIAM TUCKER MEREDITH

From Storybook and Legend

The Clerk of Oxenford

There was a Student out of Oxford town,
Indentured long to logic and the gown.
Lean as a rake the horse on which he sat,
And he himself was anything but fat,
But rather wore a hollow look and sad.
Threadbare the little outer coat he had,
For he was still to get a benefice
And thoughts of worldly office were not his.
For he would rather have beside his bed
Twenty books arrayed in black or red
Of Aristotle and his philosophy
Than robes or fiddle or jocund psaltery.
Yet though he was philosopher, his coffer
Indeed but scanty store of gold could offer,
And any he could borrow from a friend
On books and learning straightway would he spend,
And make with prayer a constant offering
For those that helped him with his studying.
He gave to study all his care and heed,
Nor ever spoke a word beyond his need,
And that was said in form, respectfully,
And brief and quick and charged with meaning high.
Harmonious with virtue was his speech,
And gladly would he learn and gladly teach.

GEOFFREY CHAUCER

Translated into modern English by Frank Ernest Hill

Ruth

She stood breast high among the corn,
Clasped by the golden light of morn,
Like the sweetheart of the sun,
Who many a glowing kiss had won.

On her cheek an autumn flush,
Deeply ripened;—such a blush
In the midst of brown was born,
Like red poppies grown with corn.

Round her eyes her tresses fell,
Which were blackest none could tell.
But long lashes veiled a light,
That had else been all too bright.

And her hat, with shady brim,
Made her tressy forehead dim;
Thus she stood amid the stooks,
Praising God with sweetest looks.—

Sure, I said, Heav'n did not mean,
Where I reap thou shouldst but glean,
Lay thy sheaf adown and come,
Share my harvest and my home.

THOMAS . HOOD

Ulysses

It little profits that an idle king,
By this still hearth, among these barren crags,
Match'd with an aged wife, I mete and dole
Unequal laws unto a savage race,
That hoard, and sleep, and feed, and know not me.
I cannot rest from travel: I will drink
Life on the lees: all times I have enjoy'd
Greatly, have suffer'd greatly, both with those
That loved me, and alone; on shore, and when
Thro' scudding drifts the rainy Hyades
Vext the dim sea: I am become a name;
For always roaming with a hungry heart.
Much have I seen and known; cities of men
And manners, climates, councils, governments,
Myself not least, but honour'd of them all;
And drunk delight of battle with my peers,
Far on the ringing plains of windy Troy.
I am a part of all that I have met;
Yet all experience is an arch wherethro'
Gleams that untravell'd world, whose margin fades
For ever and for ever when I move.
How dull it is to pause, to make an end,
To rust unburnish'd, not to shine in use!
As tho' to breathe were life. Life piled on life
Were all too little, and of one to me
Little remains: but every hour is saved
From that eternal silence, something more,
A bringer of new things; and vile it were

For some three suns to store and hoard myself,
And this gray spirit yearning in desire
To follow knowledge like a sinking star,
Beyond the utmost bound of human thought.
    This is my son, mine own Telemachus,
To whom I leave the sceptre and the isle—
Well-loved of me, discerning to fulfil
This labour, by slow prudence to make mild
A rugged people, and thro' soft degrees
Subdue them to the useful and the good.
Most blameless is he, centred in the sphere
Of common duties, decent not to fail
In offices of tenderness, and pay
Meet adoration to my household gods,
When I am gone. He works his work, I mine.
    There lies the port; the vessel puffs her sail:
There gloom the dark broad seas. My mariners,
Souls that have toil'd, and wrought, and thought with me
That ever with a frolic welcome took
The thunder and the sunshine, and opposed
Free hearts, free foreheads—you and I are old;
Old age hath yet his honour and his toil;
Death closes all: but something ere the end,
Some work of noble note, may yet be done,
Not unbecoming men that strove with Gods.
The lights begin to twinkle from the rocks:
The long day wanes: the slow moon climbs: the deep
Moans round with many voices. Come, my friends,
'Tis not too late to seek a newer world.
Push off, and sitting well in order smite
The sounding furrows; for my purpose holds

To sail beyond the sunset, and the baths
Of all the western stars, until I die.
It may be that the gulfs will wash us down:
It may be we shall touch the Happy Isles,
And see the great Achilles, whom we knew.
Tho' much is taken, much abides; and tho'
We are not now that strength which in old days
Moved earth and heaven; that which we are, we are;
One equal temper of heroic hearts,
Made weak by time and fate, but strong in will
To strive, to seek, to find, and not to yield.

ALFRED TENNYSON

Sir Galahad

My good blade carves the casques of men,
  My tough lance thrusteth sure,
My strength is as the strength of ten,
  Because my heart is pure.
The shattering trumpet shrilleth high,
  The hard brands shiver on the steel,
The splinter'd spear-shafts crack and fly,
  The horse and rider reel:
They reel, they roll in clanging lists,
  And when the tide of combat stands,
Perfume and flowers fall in showers,
  That lightly rain from ladies' hands.

How sweet are looks that ladies bend
  On whom their favours fall!
For them I battle till the end,
  To save from shame and thrall:
But all my heart is drawn above,
  My knees are bow'd in crypt and shrine:
I never felt the kiss of love,
  Nor maiden's hand in mine.
More bounteous aspects on me beam,
  Me mightier transports move and thrill;
So keep I fair thro' faith and prayer
  A virgin heart in work and will.

When down the stormy crescent goes,
  A light before me swims,

Between dark stems the forest glows,
    I hear a noise of hymns:
Then by some secret shrine I ride;
    I hear a voice but none are there;
The stalls are void, the doors are wide,
    The tapers burning fair.
Fair gleams the snowy altar-cloth,
    The silver vessels sparkle clean,
The shrill bell rings, the censer swings,
    And solemn chaunts resound between.

Sometimes on lonely mountain-meres
    I find a magic bark;
I leap on board: no helmsman steers:
    I float till all is dark.
A gentle sound, an awful light!
    Three angels bear the Holy Grail:
With folded feet, in stoles of white,
    On sleeping wings they sail.
Ah, blessed vision! blood of God!
    My spirit beats her mortal bars,
As down dark tides the glory slides,
    And star-like mingles with the stars.

When on my goodly charger borne
    Thro' dreaming towns I go,
The cock crows ere the Christmas morn,
    The streets are dumb with snow.
The tempest crackles on the leads,
    And, ringing, springs from brand and mail;
But o'er the dark a glory spreads,
    And gilds the driving hail.

I leave the plain, I climb the height;
　　No branchy thicket shelter yields;
But blessed forms in whistling storms
　　Fly o'er waste fens and windy fields.

A maiden knight—to me is given
　　Such hope, I know not fear;
I yearn to breathe the airs of heaven
　　That often meet me here.
I muse on joy that will not cease,
　　Pure spaces clothed in living beams,
Pure lilies of eternal peace,
　　Whose odours haunt my dreams;
And, stricken by an angel's hand,
　　This mortal armour that I wear,
This weight and size, this heart and eyes,
　　Are touch'd, are turn'd to finest air.

The clouds are broken in the sky,
　　And thro' the mountain-walls
A rolling organ-harmony
　　Swells up, and shakes and falls.
Then move the trees, the copses nod,
　　Wings flutter, voices hover clear:
'O just and faithful knight of God!
　　Ride on! the prize is near.'
So pass I hostel, hall and grange;
　　By bridge and ford, by park and pale,
All-arm'd I ride, whate'er betide,
　　Until I find the Holy Grail.

ALFRED TENNYSON

Robinson Crusoe's Story

The night was thick and hazy
    When the Piccadilly Daisy
Carried down the crew and the captain in the sea;
    And I think the water drowned 'em;
    For they never, never found 'em,
And I know they didn't come ashore with me.

Oh! 'twas very sad and lonely
    When I found myself the only
Population on this cultivated shore;
    But I've made a little tavern
    In a rocky little cavern,
And I sit and watch for people at the door.

I spent no time in looking
    For a girl to do my cooking,
As I'm quite a clever hand at making stews;
    But I had that fellow Friday,
    Just to keep the tavern tidy,
And to put a Sunday polish on my shoes.

I have a little garden
    That I'm cultivating lard in,
As the things I eat are rather tough and dry;
    For I live on toasted lizards,
    Prickly pears, and parrot gizzards,
And I'm really very fond of beetle pie.

The clothes I had were furry,
And it made me fret and worry
When I found the moths were eating off the hair;
    And I had to scrape and sand 'em,
    And I boiled 'em and I tanned 'em,
Till I got the fine morocco suit I wear.

    I sometimes seek diversion
    In a family excursion
With the few domestic animals you see;
    And we take along a carrot
    As refreshment for the parrot,
And a little can of jungleberry tea.

    Then we gather, as we travel,
    Bits of moss and dirty gravel,
And we chip off little specimens of stone;
    And we carry home as prizes
    Funny bugs, of handy sizes,
Just to give the day a scientific tone.

    If the roads are wet and muddy,
    We remain at home and study,—
For the Goat is very clever at a sum,—
    And the Dog, instead of fighting,
    Studies ornamental writing,
While the Cat is taking lessons on the drum.

We retire at eleven,
And we rise again at seven;
And I wish to call attention, as I close,
To the fact that all the scholars
Are correct about their collars,
And particular in turning out their toes.

CHARLES   EDWARD   CARRYL

Don Juan Declaims

I am Don Juan, curst from age to age
By priestly tract and sentimental stage:
Branded a villain or believed a fool,
Battered by hatred, seared by ridicule,
Noble on earth, all but a king in Hell,
I am Don Juan with a tale to tell.
   Hot leapt the dawn from deep Plutonian fires
And ran like blood among the twinkling spires.
The market quickened: carts came rattling down:
Good human music roared about the town,
"And come," they cried, "and buy the best of Spain's
Great fireskinned fruits with cold and streaming veins!
Others, "The man who'd make a lordly dish,
Would buy my speckled or my silver fish."
And some, "I stitch you raiment to the rule!"
And some, "I sell you attar of Stamboul!"
"And I have lapis for your love to wear,
Pearls for her neck and amber for her hair."
Death has its gleam. They swing before me still,
The shapes and sounds and colors of Seville!
   For there I learnt to love the plot, the fight,
The masker's cloak, the ladder set for flight,
The stern pursuit, the rapier's glint of death,
The scent of starlit roses, beauty's breath,
The music and the passion and the prize,
Aragon lips and Andalusian eyes.
This day a democrat I scoured the town;
Courting, the next, I brought a princess down:

Now in some lady's panelled chamber hid
Achieved what love approves and laws forbid,
Now walked and whistled round the sleepy farms
And clasped a Dulcinea in my arms.

  I was the true, the grand idealist:
My light could pierce the pretty golden mist
That hides from common souls the starrier climes:
I loved as small men do ten thousand times:
Rose to the blue triumphant, curved my bow,
Set high the mark and brought an angel low,
And laced with that brave body and shining soul
Learnt how to live, then learnt to love the whole.
And first I broke that jungle dark and dense,
Which hides the silver house of Commonsense,
And dissipated that disastrous lie
Which makes a god of stuffless Unity,
And drave the dark behind me, and revealed
A Pagan sunrise on a Christian field.

  My legend tells how once, by passion moved,
I slew the father of a girl I loved,
Then summoned—like an old and hardened sinner—
The brand-new statue of the dead to dinner.
My ribald guests, with Spanish wine aflame,
Were most delighted when the statue came,
Bowed to the party, made a little speech,
And bore me off beyond their human reach.
Well, priests must flourish and the truth must pale:
A very pious, entertaining tale.

  But this believe. I struck a ringing blow
At sour Authority's ancestral show,
And stirred the sawdust understuffing all

The sceptred or the surpliced ritual.
I willed my happiness, kept bright and brave
My thoughts and deeds this side of the accursed grave.
Life was a ten-course banquet after all,
And neatly rounded by my funeral.
"Pale guest, why strip the roses from your brow?
We hope to feast till morning." "Who knocks now?"
"Twelve of the clock, Don Juan." In he came,
That shining, tall and cold Authority,
Whose marble lips smile down on lips that pray,
And took my hand, and I was led away.

JAMES ELROY FLECKER

Deirdre

Do not let any woman read this verse!
It is for men, and after them their sons,
And their sons' sons!

The time comes when our hearts sink utterly;
When we remember Deirdre, and her tale,
And that her lips are dust.

Once she did tread the earth: men took her hand;
They looked into her eyes and said their say,
And she replied to them.

More than two thousand years it is since she
Was beautiful: she trod the waving grass;
She saw the clouds.

Two thousand years! The grass is still the same;
The clouds as lovely as they were that time
When Deirdre was alive.

But there has been again no woman born
Who was so beautiful; not one so beautiful
Of all the women born.

Let all men go apart and mourn together!
No man can ever love her! Not a man
Can dream to be her lover!

No man can bend before her! No man say—
What could one say to her? There are no words
That one could say to her!

Now she is but a story that is told
Beside the fire! No man can ever be
The friend of that poor queen!

JAMES STEPHENS

Meg Merrilies

Old Meg she was a gipsy;
   And lived upon the moors:
Her bed it was the brown heath turf,
   And her house was out of doors.
Her apples were swart blackberries,
   Her currants, pods o'broom;
Her wine was dew of the wild, white rose,
   Her book a church-yard tomb.

Her brothers were the craggy hills,
   Her sisters larchen trees;
Alone with her great family
   She lived as she did please.
No breakfast had she many a morn,
   No dinner many a noon,
And, 'stead of supper, she would stare
   Full hard against the moon.

But every morn, of woodbine fresh
   She made her garlanding,
And every night, the dark glen yew
   She wove and she would sing.
And with her fingers, old and brown,
   She plaited mats of rushes,
And gave them to the cottagers
   She met among the bushes.

Old Meg was brave as Margaret Queen,
  And tall as Amazon;
An old red blanket cloak she wore,
  A ship-hat had she on:
God rest her aged bones somewhere!
  She died full long agone!

JOHN KEATS

Aladdin and the Jinn

"Bring me soft song," said Aladdin;
"This tailor-shop sings not at all.
Chant me a word of the twilight,
Of roses that mourn in the fall.
Bring me a song like hashish
That will comfort the stale and the sad,
For I would be mending my spirit,
Forgetting these days that are bad:
Forgetting companions too shallow,
Their quarrels and arguments thin;
Forgetting the shouting muezzin."
"*I am your slave*," said the Jinn.

"Bring me old wines," said Aladdin,
"I have been a starved pauper too long.
Serve them in vessels of jade and of shell,
Serve them with fruit and with song:
Wines of pre-Adamite Sultans
Digged from beneath the black seas,
New-gathered dew from the heavens
Dripped down from heaven's sweet trees,
Cups from the angels' pale tables
That will make me both handsome and wise;
For I have beheld her, the Princess—
Firelight and starlight her eyes!
Pauper I am—I would woo her.
And . . . let me drink wine to begin,
Though the Koran expressly forbids it."
"*I am your slave*," said the Jinn.

"Plan me a dome," said Aladdin,
   "That is drawn like the dawn of the moon,
When the sphere seems to rest on the mountains
   Half-hidden, yet full-risen soon.
Build me a dome," said Aladdin,
   "That shall cause all young lovers to sigh—
The fullness of life and of beauty,
   Peace beyond peace to the eye;
A palace of foam and of opal,
   Pure moonlight without and within,
Where I may enthrone my sweet lady."
   "*I am your slave*," said the Jinn.

VACHEL LINDSAY

Some Strange Characters

Captain Jinks

I'm Captain Jinks of the Horse Marines,
I feed my horse on corn and beans,
And sport young ladies in their teens,
    Though a captain in the army.
I teach young ladies how to dance,
How to dance, how to dance,
I teach young ladies how to dance,
    For I'm the pet of the army.

      Captain Jinks of the Horse Marines,
      I feed my horse on corn and beans,
      And often live beyond my means,
          Though a captain in the army.

I joined my corps when twenty-one,
Of course I thought it capital fun;
When the enemy comes of course I run,
    For I'm not cut out for the army.
When I left home, mama she cried,
Mama she cried, mama she cried,
When I left home, mama she cried:
    "He's not cut out for the army."

      Captain Jinks of the Horse Marines,
      I feed my horse on corn and beans,
      And often live beyond my means,
          Though a captain in the army.

The first time I went out to drill,
The bugle sounding made me ill;
Of the battle field I'd had my fill,
  For I'm not cut out for the army.
The officers they all did shout,
They all did shout, they all did shout,
The officers they all did shout:
  "Why, kick him out of the army."

Captain Jinks of the Horse Marines,
I feed my horse on corn and beans,
And often live beyond my means,
  Though a captain in the army.

ANONYMOUS

The Duke of Plaza-Toro

In enterprise of martial kind,
   When there was any fighting,
He led his regiment from behind—
   He found it less exciting.
But when away his regiment ran,
   His place was at the fore, O—
        That celebrated,
        Cultivated,
        Underrated
           Nobleman,
   The Duke of Plaza-Toro!

In the first and foremost flight, ha, ha!
You always found that knight, ha, ha!
        That celebrated,
        Cultivated,
        Underrated
           Nobleman,
   The Duke of Plaza-Toro!

When to evade Destruction's hand,
   To hide they all proceeded,
No soldier in that gallant band
   Hid half as well as he did.
He lay concealed throughout the war,
   And so preserved his gore, O!

That unaffected,
Undetected,
Well-connected
Warrior,
The Duke of Plaza-Toro!

In every doughty deed, ha, ha!
He always took the lead, ha, ha!
That unaffected,
Undetected,
Well-connected
Warrior,
The Duke of Plaza-Toro!

When told that they would all be shot
Unless they left the service,
That hero hesitated not,
So marvellous his nerve is.
He sent his resignation in,
The first of all his corps, O!
That very knowing,
Overflowing,
Easy-going
Paladin,
The Duke of Plaza-Toro!

To men of grosser clay, ha, ha!
He always showed the way, ha, ha!

That very knowing,
Overflowing,
Easy-going
            Paladin,
The Duke of Plaza-Toro!

W. S. GILBERT

The Major-General

I am the very model of a modern Major-General,
I've information vegetable, animal, and mineral,
I know the kings of England, and I quote the fights histori
    cal,
From Marathon to Waterloo, in order categorical;
I'm very well acquainted too with matters mathematical,
I understand equations, both the simple and quadratica
About binomial theorem I'm teeming with a lot of news—
With many cheerful facts about the square of the hypote
    nuse.
I'm very good at integral and differential calculus,
I know the scientific names of beings animalculous,
In short, in matters vegetable, animal, and mineral,
I am the very model of a modern Major-General.

I know our mythic history, King Arthur's and Sir Caradoc's
I answer hard acrostics, I've a pretty taste for paradox,
I quote in elegiacs all the crimes of Heliogabalus,
In conics I can floor peculiarities parabolous.
I can tell undoubted Raphaels from Gerard Dows and Zof
    fanies,
I know the croaking chorus from the *Frogs* of Aristophanes
Then I can hum a fugue of which I've heard the music's di
    afore,
And whistle all the airs from that infernal nonsense *Pina*
    fore.
Then I can write a washing bill in Babylonic cuneiform,
And tell you every detail of Caractacus's uniform;

n short, in matters vegetable, animal, and mineral,
 am the very model of a modern Major-General.

n fact, when I know what is meant by "mamelon" and
   "ravelin",
Vhen I can tell at sight a chassepôt rifle from a javelin,
Vhen such affairs as sorties and surprises I'm more wary at,
And when I know precisely what is meant by "commis-
   sariat",
Vhen I have learnt what progress has been made in modern
   gunnery,
Vhen I know more of tactics than a novice in a nunnery:
n short, when I've a smattering of elemental strategy,
'ou'll say a better Major-General has never *sat* a gee—
'or my military knowledge, though I'm plucky and ad-
   ventury,
Ias only been brought down to the beginning of the century;
But still in matters vegetable, animal, and mineral,
 am the very model of a modern Major-General.

W. S. GILBERT

Father William

"You are old, father William," the young man said,
   "And your hair has become very white;
And yet you incessantly stand on your head—
   Do you think, at your age, it is right?"

"In my youth," father William replied to his son,
   "I feared it might injure the brain;
But now that I'm perfectly sure I have none,
   Why, I do it again and again."

"You are old," said the youth, "as I mentioned before,
   And have grown most uncommonly fat;
Yet you turned a back-somersault in at the door—
   Pray what is the reason of that?"

"In my youth," said the sage, as he shook his grey locks,
   "I kept all my limbs very supple
By the use of this ointment—one shilling the box—
   Allow me to sell you a couple."

"You are old," said the youth, "and your jaws are too weak
   For anything tougher than suet;
Yet you finished the goose, with the bones and the beak—
   Pray, how did you manage to do it?"

"In my youth," said his father, "I took to the law,
   And argued each case with my wife;
And the muscular strength, which it gave to my jaw,
   Has lasted the rest of my life."

"You are old," said the youth, "one would hardly suppose
 That your eye was as steady as ever;
Yet you balanced an eel on the end of your nose—
 What made you so awfully clever?"

"I have answered three questions, and that is enough,"
 Said his father; "Don't give yourself airs!
Do you think I can listen all day to such stuff?
 Be off, or I'll kick you downstairs!"

LEWIS CARROLL

The Aged Aged Man

I'll tell thee everything I can:
    There's little to relate.
I saw an aged aged man,
    A-sitting on a gate.
'Who are you, aged man?' I said,
    'And how is it you live?'
And his answer trickled through my head,
    Like water through a sieve.

He said 'I look for butterflies
    That sleep among the wheat:
I make them into mutton pies,
    And sell them in the street.
I sell them unto men,' he said,
    'Who sail on stormy seas;
And that's the way I get my bread—
    A trifle, if you please.'

But I was thinking of a plan
    To dye one's whiskers green,
And always use so large a fan
    That they could not be seen.
So, having no reply to give
    To what the old man said,
I cried 'Come, tell me how you live!'
    And thumped him on the head.

His accents mild took up the tale:
    He said 'I go my ways,

And when I find a mountain-rill,
    I set it in a blaze;
And thence they make a stuff they call
    Rowland's Macassar-Oil—
Yet twopence-halfpenny is all
    They give me for my toil.'

But I was thinking of a way
    To feed oneself on batter,
And so go on from day to day
    Getting a little fatter.
I shook him well from side to side,
    Until his face was blue:
'Come, tell me how you live,' I cried,
    'And what it is you do!'

He said 'I hunt for haddocks' eyes
    Among the heather bright,
And work them into waistcoat-buttons
    In the silent night.
And these I do not sell for gold
    Or coin of silvery shine,
But for a copper halfpenny,
    And that will purchase nine.

'I sometimes dig for buttered rolls,
    Or set limed twigs for crabs:
I sometimes search the grassy knolls
    For wheels of Hansom-cabs.
And that's the way' (he gave a wink)
    'By which I get my wealth—

And very gladly will I drink
　　Your Honour's noble health.'

I heard him then, for I had just
　　Completed my design
To keep the Menai bridge from rust
　　By boiling it in wine.
I thanked him much for telling me
　　The way he got his wealth,
But chiefly for his wish that he
　　Might drink my noble health.

And now, if e'er by chance I put
　　My fingers into glue,
Or madly squeeze a right-hand foot
　　Into a left-hand shoe,
Or if I drop upon my toe
　　A very heavy weight,
I weep, for it reminds me so
Of that old man I used to know—
Whose look was mild, whose speech was slow,
Whose hair was whiter than the snow,
Whose face was very like a crow,
With eyes, like cinders, all aglow,
Who seemed distracted by his woe,
Who rocked his body to and fro,
And muttered mumblingly and low,
As if his mouth were full of dough,
Who snorted like a buffalo—
That summer evening long ago,
　　A-sitting on a gate.

LEWIS CARROLL

The King of Yvetot

There was a king of Yvetot,
  Of whom renown hath little said,
Who let all thoughts of glory go,
  And dawdled half his days a-bed;
And every night, as night came round,
By Jenny, with a nightcap crowned,
     Slept very sound.
  Sing ho, ho, ho! and he, he, he!
  That's the kind of king for me.

And every day it came to pass
  That four lusty meals made he;
And step by step, upon an ass,
  Rode abroad his realms to see;
And wherever he did stir,
What think you was his escort, sir?
     Why, an old cur.
  Sing ho, ho, ho! and he, he, he!
  That's the kind of king for me.

To all the ladies of the land,
  A courteous king, and kind, was he;
The reason why you'll understand,
  They named him *Pater Patriae*.
Each year he called his fighting men
And marched a league from home, and then
     Marched back again.
  Sing ho, ho, ho! and he, he, he!
  That's the kind of king for me.

The portrait of this best of kings
   Is standing still, upon a sign
That on a village tavern swings,
   Famed in the country for good wine.
The people in their Sunday trim,
Filling their glasses to the brim,
     Look up to him,
   Singing ho, ho, ho! and he, he, he!
   That's the kind of king for me.

WILLIAM MAKEPEACE THACKERAY

From the French of Béranger

The New Vestments

There lived an old man in the Kingdom of Tess,
Who invented a purely original dress;
And when it was perfectly made and complete,
He opened the door and walked into the street.

By way of a hat he'd a loaf of Brown Bread,
In the middle of which he inserted his head;
His Shirt was made up of no end of dead Mice,
The warmth of whose skins was quite fluffy and nice;
His Drawers were of Rabbit-skins, so were his Shoes;
His Stockings were skins, but it is not known whose;
His Waistcoat and Trowsers were made of Pork Chops;
His Buttons were Jujubes and Chocolate Drops;
His Coat was all Pancakes, with Jam for a border,
And a girdle of Biscuits to keep it in order;
And he wore over all, as a screen from bad weather,
A Cloak of green Cabbage-leaves stitched all together.

He had walked a short way, when he heard a great noise,
Of all sorts of Beasticles, Birdlings, and Boys;
And from every long street and dark lane in the town
Beasts, Birdles, and Boys in a tumult rushed down.
Two Cows and a Calf ate his Cabbage-leaf Cloak;
Four Apes seized his Girdle, which vanished like smoke;
Three Kids ate up half of his Pancaky Coat,
And the tails were devour'd by an ancient He Goat;
An army of Dogs in a twinkling tore *up* his
Pork Waistcoat and Trowsers to give to their Puppies;

And while they were growling and mumbling the Chops,
Ten Boys prigged the Jujubes and Chocolate Drops.
He tried to run back to his house, but in vain,
For scores of fat pigs came again and again:
They rushed out of stables and hovels and doors;
They tore off his stockings, his shoes, and his drawers;
And now from the housetops with screechings descend
Striped, spotted, white, black, and grey cats without end:
They jumped on his shoulders and knocked off his hat,
When Crows, Ducks, and Hens made a mincemeat of that;
They speedily flew at his sleeves in a trice,
And utterly tore up his Shirt of dead Mice;
They swallowed the last of his shirt with a squall,—
Whereon he ran home with no clothes on at all.

And he said to himself, as he bolted the door,
"I will not wear a similar dress any more,
Any more, any more, any more, never more!"

EDWARD LEAR

194

The Akond of Swat

Who, or why, or which, or *what,*
                         Is the Akond of SWAT?

Is he tall, or short, or dark or fair?
Does he sit on a stool or a sofa or chair,
                         Or SQUAT?
                         The Akond of Swat?

Is he wise or foolish, young or old?
Does he drink his soup and his coffee cold,
                         Or HOT,
                         The Akond of Swat?

Does he sing or whistle, jabber or talk,
And when riding abroad does he gallop or walk,
                         Or TROT,
                         The Akond of Swat?

Does he wear a turban, a fez, or a hat?
Does he sleep on a mattress, a bed, or a mat,
                         Or a COT,
                         The Akond of Swat?

When he writes a copy in round-hand size
Does he cross his T's and finish his I's
                         with a DOT,
                         The Akond of Swat?

Can he write a letter concisely clear
Without a speck or a smudge or smear
                      or BLOT,
                  The Akond of Swat?

Do his people like him extremely well?
Or do they, whenever they can, rebel,
                      or PLOT,
               At the Akond of Swat?

If he catches them then, either old or young,
Does he have them chopped in pieces or hung,
                      or SHOT,
                  The Akond of Swat?

Do his people prig in the lanes or park?
Or even at times, when days are dark,
                  GAROTTE?
               O the Akond of Swat!

Does he study the wants of his own dominion?
Or doesn't he care for public opinion
                     a JOT,
                  The Akond of Swat?

To amuse his mind do his people show him
Pictures, or any one's last new poem,
                    or WHAT,
              For the Akond of Swat?

At night if he suddenly screams and wakes,
Do they bring him only a few small cakes,
                              or a LOT,
                    For the Akond of Swat?

Does he live on turnips, tea, or tripe?
Does he like his shawl to be marked with a stripe,
                              or a DOT,
                    The Akond of Swat?

Does he like to lie on his back in a boat
Like the lady who lived in that isle remote,
                              SHALOTT
                    The Akond of Swat?

Is he quiet or always making a fuss?
Is his steward a Swiss or a Swede or a Russ,
                              or a SCOT
                    The Akond of Swat?

Does he like to sit by the calm blue wave?
Or to sleep and snore in a dark green cave,
                              or a GROTT,
                    The Akond of Swat?

Does he drink small beer from a silver jug?
Or a bowl? or a glass? or a cup? or a mug?
                              or a POT,
                    The Akond of Swat?

Does he beat his wife with a gold-topped pipe,
When she lets the gooseberries grow too ripe,
                              or ROT,
                    The Akond of Swat?

Does he wear a white tie when he dines with friends,
And tie it neat in a bow with ends,
                              or a KNOT,
                    The Akond of Swat?

Does he like new cream and hate mince-pies?
When he looks at the sun does he wink his eyes,
                              or NOT,
                    The Akond of Swat?

Does he teach his subjects to roast and bake?
Does he sail about on an inland lake,
                              in a YACHT,
                    The Akond of Swat?

Some one, or nobody, knows I wot
Who or which or why or what
                    Is the Akond of Swat!

EDWARD LEAR

The Sluggard

'Tis the voice of the sluggard; I heard him complain,
'You have waked me too soon, I must slumber again.'
As the door on its hinges, so he on his bed,
Turns his sides and his shoulders and his heavy head.

'A little more sleep and a little more slumber;'
Thus he wastes half his days and his hours without number;
And when he gets up, he sits folding his hands,
Or walks about saunt'ring, or trifling he stands.

I pass'd by his garden, and saw the wild briar,
The thorn and the thistle grow broader and higher;
The clothes that hang on him are turning to rags;
And his money still wastes, till he starves or he begs.

I made him a visit, still hoping to find
He had took better care for improving his mind:
He told me his dreams, talked of eating and drinking;
But he scarce reads his Bible, and never loves thinking.

ISAAC WATTS

Elegy on Mrs. Mary Blaize

Good People all, with one accord,
   Lament for Madam Blaize,
Who never wanted a good word—
   From those who spoke her praise.

The needy seldom passed her door,
   And always found her kind;
She freely lent to all the poor—
   Who left a pledge behind.

She strove the neighborhood to please,
   With manners wondrous winning;
And never followed wicked ways—
   Unless when she was sinning.

At church, in silks and satins new,
   With hoop of monstrous size;
She never slumbered in her pew—
   But when she shut her eyes.

Her love was sought, I do aver,
   By twenty beaux and more;
The king himself has followed her—
   When she has walked before.

But now her wealth and finery fled,
   Her hangers-on cut short all;
The doctors found, when she was dead—
   Her last disorder mortal.

Let us lament, in sorrow sore,
  For Kent Street well may say
That had she lived a twelvemonth more—
  She had not died today.

OLIVER GOLDSMITH

Limericks

I

There was a young man so benighted,
He never knew when he was slighted.
    He went to a party,
    And ate just as hearty
As if he'd been really invited.

II

There was a young lady of Lynn,
Who was so uncommonly thin
    That when she essayed
    To drink lemonade,
She slipped through the straw and fell in.

III

There was a young maid of Manila,
Whose favorite cream was vanilla,
    But sad to relate,
    Though you piled up her plate,
'Twas impossible ever to fill her.

IV

There was a young man down in Ga.,
As cunning and cold as a Ba.
    But he shuffled the decks,
    Wrote many false checks,
And now he's in jail as a fa.

ANONYMOUS

I

'I quite realized,' said Columbus,
'That the earth was not a rhombus,
'But I *am* a little annoyed
'To find it an oblate spheroid.'

II

Among the contemporaries of Shakespeare
They were few who regarded him as Drake's peer.
Spoiling paper was so much less strain
Than spoiling the Spanish Main.

III

It was a rule of Leonardo da Vinci's
Not to put his trust in princes.
Pleading was of no avail;
They had to pay up on the nail.

IV

It was a weakness of Voltaire's,
To forget to say his prayers,
And one which to his shame
He never overcame.

EDMUND CLERIHEW BENTLEY

The Reformation of Godfrey Gore

GODFREY GORDON GUSTAVUS GORE—
No doubt you have heard the name before—
Was a boy who never would shut a door!

The wind might whistle, the wind might roar,
And teeth be aching and throats be sore,
But still he never would shut the door.

His father would beg, his mother implore,
"Godfrey Gordon Gustavus Gore,
We really *do* wish you would shut the door!"

Their hands they wrung, their hair they tore;
But Godfrey Gordon Gustavus Gore
Was deaf as the buoy out at the Nore.

When he walked forth the folks would roar,
"Godfrey Gordon Gustavus Gore,
Why don't you think to shut the door?"

They rigged out a Shutter with sail and oar,
And threatened to pack off Gustavus Gore
On a voyage of penance to Singapore.

But he begged for mercy, and said, "No more!
Pray do not send me to Singapore
On a Shutter, and then I will shut the door!"

"You will?" said his parents; "then keep on shore!
But mind you do! For the plague is sore
Of a fellow that never will shut the door,
Godfrey Gordon Gustavus Gore!"

WILLIAM BRIGHTLY RANDS

The Poet
Himself

Ode on Solitude

Happy the man whose wish and care
   A few paternal acres bound,
Content to breathe his native air,
            In his own ground.

Whose herds with milk, whose fields with bread,
   Whose flocks supply him with attire,
Whose trees in summer yield him shade,
            In winter fire.

Bless'd, who can unconcern'dly find
   Hours, days, and years slide soft away,
In health of body, peace of mind,
            Quiet by day;

Sound sleep by night; study and ease
   Together mix'd; sweet recreation;
And innocence, which most does please
            With meditation.

Thus let me live, unseen, unknown,
   Thus unlamented let me die,
Steal from the world, and not a stone
            Tell where I lie.

ALEXANDER POPE

Contentment

"Man wants but little here below"

Little I ask; my wants are few;
    I only wish a hut of stone
(A *very plain* brownstone will do),
    That I may call my own:—
And close at hand is such a one,
In yonder street that fronts the sun.

Plain food is quite enough for me;
    Three courses are as good as ten;—
If Nature can subsist on three,
    Thank Heaven for three. Amen!
I always thought cold victual nice;—
My *choice* would be vanilla-ice.

I care not much for gold or land;—
    Give me a mortgage here and there,—
Some good bank-stock, some note of hand,
    Or a trifling railroad share,—
I only ask that Fortune send
A little more than I shall spend.

Honors are silly toys, I know,
    And titles are but empty names;
I would, *perhaps*, be Plenipo,—
    But only near St. James;
I'm very sure I should not care
To fill our Gubernator's chair.

Jewels are bawbles; 'tis a sin
    To care for such unfruitful things;—
One good-sized diamond in a pin,—
    Some, *not so large*, in rings,
A ruby, and a pearl, or so,
Will do for me;—I laugh at show.

My dame should dress in cheap attire;
    (Good, heavy silks are never dear;)
I own perhaps I *might* desire
    Some shawls of true Cashmere,—
Some marrowy crapes of China silk,
Like wrinkled skins on scalded milk.

I would not have the horse I drive
    So fast that folks must stop and stare;
An easy gait—two forty-five—
    Suits me; I do not care;—
Perhaps, for just a *single spurt*,
Some seconds less would do no hurt.

Of pictures, I should like to own
    Titians and Raphaels three or four,—
I love so much their style and tone,—
    One Turner, and no more,
(A landscape,—foreground golden dirt,—
The sunshine painted with a squirt.)

Of books but few,—some fifty score
    For daily use, and bound for wear;
The rest upon an upper floor;—

Some *little* luxury *there*
Of red morocco's gilded gleam,
And vellum rich as country cream.

Busts, cameos, gems,—such things as these
    Which others often show for pride,
I value for their power to please,
    And selfish churls deride;—
One Stradivarius, I confess,
Two meerschaums, I would fain possess.

Wealth's wasteful tricks I will not learn
    Nor ape the glittering upstart fool;—
Shall not carved tables serve my turn,
    But all must be of buhl?
Give grasping pomp its double share,—
I ask but one recumbent chair.

Thus humble let me live and die,
    Nor long for Midas's golden touch;
If Heaven more generous gifts deny,
    I shall not miss them *much*,—
Too grateful for the blessing lent
Of simple tastes and mind content!

OLIVER WENDELL HOLMES

By Way of Preface

'How pleasant to know Mr. Lear!'
    Who has written such volumes of stuff!
Some think him ill-tempered and queer,
    But a few think him pleasant enough.

His mind is concrete and fastidious,
    His nose is remarkably big;
His visage is more or less hideous,
    His beard it resembles a wig.

He has ears, and two eyes, and ten fingers,
    Leastways if you reckon two thumbs;
Long ago he was one of the singers,
    But now he is one of the dumbs.

He sits in a beautiful parlor,
    With hundreds of books on the wall;
He drinks a great deal of Marsala,
    But never gets tipsy at all.

He has many friends, laymen and clerical,
    Old Foss is the name of his cat:
His body is perfectly spherical,
    He weareth a runcible hat.

When he walks in a waterproof white,
    The children run after him so!
Calling out, 'He's come out in his night-
    gown, that crazy old Englishman, oh!'

He weeps by the side of the ocean,
    He weeps on the top of the hill;
He purchases pancakes and lotion,
    And chocolate shrimps from the mill.

He reads, but he cannot speak Spanish,
    He cannot abide ginger-beer:
Ere the days of his pilgrimage vanish,
    How pleasant to know Mr. Lear!

EDWARD LEAR

There Was a Child Went Forth

There was a child went forth every day,
And the first object he look'd upon, that object he became,
And that object became part of him for the day or a certain
    part of the day,
Or for many years or stretching cycles of years.

The early lilacs became part of this child,
And grass, and white and red morning-glories, and white and
    red clover, and the song of the phœbe-bird,
And the Third-month lambs and the sow's pink-faint litter,
    and the mare's foal and the cow's calf,
And the noisy brood of the barnyard or by the mire of the
    pond-side,
And the fish suspending themselves so curiously below there,
    and the beautiful curious liquid,
And the water-plants with their graceful flat heads, all be-
    came part of him.

The field-sprouts of Fourth-month and Fifth-month be-
    came part of him,
Winter-grain sprouts and those of the light-yellow corn, and
    the esculent roots of the garden,
And the apple-trees cover'd with blossoms and the fruit
    afterward, and wood-berries, and the commonest weeds
    by the road,
And the old drunkard staggering home from the outhouse of
    the tavern whence he had lately risen,

And the schoolmistress that pass'd on her way to the scho[o]
And the friendly boys that pass'd, and the quarrelsome bo[ys]
And the tidy and fresh-cheek'd girls, and the barefoot neg[ro]
    boy and girl,
And all the changes of city and country wherever he went.

His own parents, he that had father'd him and she that h[ad]
    conceiv'd him in her womb and birth'd him,
They gave this child more of themselves than that,
They gave him afterward every day, they became part [of]
    him.

The mother at home quietly placing the dishes on the su[p]-
    per-table,
The mother with mild words, clean her cap and gown,
    wholesome odor falling off her person and clothes [as]
    she walks by,
The father, strong, self-sufficient, manly, mean, anger'd, u[n]-
    just,
The blow, the quick loud word, the tight bargain, the craf[ty]
    lure,
The family usages, the language, the company, the furnitu[re,]
    the yearning and swelling heart,
Affection that will not be gainsay'd, the sense of what is re[al,]
    the thought if after all it should prove unreal,
The doubts of day-time and the doubts of night-time, t[he]
    curious whether and how,
Whether that which appears so is so, or is it all flashes a[nd]
    specks?
Men and women crowding fast in the streets, if they are n[ot]
    flashes and specks what are they?

he streets themselves and the façades of houses, and goods
   in the windows,
vehicles, teams, the heavy-plank'd wharves, the huge cross-
   ing at the ferries,
the village on the highland seen from afar at sunset, the
   river between,
shadows, aureola and mist, the light falling on roofs and
   gables of white or brown two miles off,
the schooner near by sleepily dropping down the tide, the
   little boat slack-tow'd astern,
the hurrying tumbling waves, quick-broken crests, slapping,
the strata of color'd clouds, the long bar of maroon-tint
   away solitary by itself, the spread of purity it lies motionless in,
the horizon's edge, the flying sea-crow, the fragrance of salt
   marsh and shore mud,
these became part of that child who went forth every day,
   and who now goes, and will always go forth every day.

On This Day I Complete My Thirty-sixth Year

'Tis time this heart should be unmoved,
  Since others it hath ceased to move:
Yet, though I cannot be beloved,
  Still let me love!

My days are in the yellow leaf;
  The flowers and fruits of love are gone;
The worm, the canker, and the grief
  Are mine alone!

The fire that on my bosom preys
  Is lone as some volcanic isle;
No torch is kindled at its blaze—
  A funeral pile.

The hope, the fear, the jealous care,
  The exalted portion of the pain
And power of love, I cannot share,
  But wear the chain.

But 'tis not *thus*—and 'tis not *here*—
  Such thoughts should shake my soul, nor *now*,
Where glory decks the hero's bier,
  Or binds his brow.

The sword, the banner, and the field,
  Glory and Greece, around me see!
The Spartan, borne upon his shield,
  Was not more free.

Awake! (not Greece—she is awake!)
    Awake, my spirit! Think through *whom*
Thy life-blood tracks its parent lake,
    And then strike home!

Tread those reviving passions down,
    Unworthy manhood!—unto thee
Indifferent should the smile or frown
    Of beauty be.

If thou regret'st thy youth, *why live?*
    The land of honorable death
Is here:—up to the field, and give
    Away thy breath!

Seek out—less often sought than found—
    A soldier's grave, for thee the best;
Then look around, and choose thy ground,
    And take thy rest.

LORD BYRON

The Vagabond

Give to me the life I love,
    Let the lave go by me,
Give the jolly heaven above
    And the byway nigh me.
Bed in the bush with stars to see,
    Bread I dip in the river—
There's the life for a man like me,
    There's the life for ever.

Let the blow fall soon or late,
    Let what will be o'er me;
Give the face of earth around
    And the road before me.
Wealth I seek not, hope nor love,
    Nor a friend to know me;
All I seek, the heaven above
    And the road below me.

Or let autumn fall on me
    Where afield I linger,
Silencing the bird on tree,
    Biting the blue finger.
White as meal the frosty field—
    Warm the fireside haven—
Not to autumn will I yield,
    Not to winter even!

Let the blow fall soon or late,
  Let what will be o'er me;
Give the face of earth around,
  And the road before me.
Wealth I ask not, hope nor love,
  Nor a friend to know me;
All I ask, the heaven above
  And the road below me.

ROBERT LOUIS STEVENSON

Finis

I strove with none; for none was worth my strife;
    Nature I loved, and next to Nature, Art;
I warmed both hands before the fire of life;
    It sinks, and I am ready to depart.

WALTER SAVAGE LANDOR

INDEX

Index of Authors

Index of Titles

228

Index of First Lines

Happy the man, whose wish and care, 209
Here blooms the flower, 136
Here lies a most beautiful lady, 41
Here lies our Sovereign Lord the King, 139
Her thoughts are like a flock of butterflies, 42
How pleasant to know Mr. Lear, 213

I am Don Juan, curst from age to age, 168
I am dying, Egypt, dying, 125
I am monarch of all I survey, 142
I am the very model of a modern Major-General, 184
I cannot say why, 149
I go to concert, party, ball, 19
I'll sing you a good old song, 118
I'll tell thee everything I can, 188
I'm Captain Jinks of the Horse Marines, 179
In enterprise of martial kind, 181
"I quite realized," said Columbus, 203
I saw him once before, 111
Is my team ploughing, 79
I strove with none, for none was worth my strife, 222
It is portentous, and a thing of state, 147
It little profits that an idle king, 159
I went to the dances at Chandlerville, 57

John Popham had a face like leather, 99

'Little Blue-Ribbons!' We call her that, 4
Little I ask; my wants are few, 210

Mary O'Brian is old and she wears a black shawl, 116
Miniver Cheevy, child of scorn, 69
My good blade carves the casques of men, 162
My mother's hands are cool and fair, 50

There was a little girl, who had a little curl, 24
There was a Student out of Oxford town, 157
There was a young man so benighted, 202
There were two little girls, neither handsome nor plain, 22
Three summers since I chose a maid, 73
Three years she grew in sun and shower, 28
'Tis the voice of the sluggard; I heard him complain, 199
'Tis time this heart should be unmoved, 218
'Twas a jolly old pedagogue, long ago, 47

Under a spreading chestnut tree, 53
Underneath this marble hearse, 138
Under yonder beech-tree single on the green-sward, 33

We are two travellers, Roger and I, 90
When I am tired of earnest men, 55
When laughing Ann comes down the street, 38
When Richard Cory went down town, 71
When Susan's work was done, she'd sit, 115
When the Norn Mother saw the Whirlwind Hour, 145
When the sheep are in the fauld, and the kye at hame, 83
Who is Silvia? What is she, 27
Who, or why, or which, or *what*, 195
With blackest moss the flower-pots, 63

"You are old, father William," the young man said, 186
You'd think I'd hate the hills?—well, this life brings, 88